Crime &

punishment

Famous
Crimes and Trials in
Truth and Fiction

Editorial Director: Susan C. Thies
Editor: Paula J. Reece
Contributing Writer: Lynn Baldini
Book Design: Jann Williams
Production: Mark Hagenberg
Photo Research: Lisa Lorimor

Image Credits

AP/Wide World Photos: 61, 67, 75, 82, 84, 98, 104, 106, 112, 121, 123
Bureau of Engraving and Printing: 116
Corbis: Cover
Dynamic Graphics: 4
Library of Congress: 6–7, 68, 94–95,
Photodisc: 56–57
Special Collections: Photographic Archives, University of Louisville: 76
www.arttoday.com: 8, 10, 20, 22, 29, 31, 39, 43, 58, 96

For information, contact
Perfection Learning® Corporation
1000 North Second Avenue, P.O. Box 500
Logan, Iowa 51546-0500.
Phone: 800-831-4190 • Fax: 712-644-2392
perfectionlearning.com

ISBN 0-7891-5562-1
Printed in the U.S.A.
4 5 6 7 PP 09 08 07 06 05

contents

UNIT ONE—

classic criminal capers

The Redheaded League

A story by Sir Arthur
Conan Doyle

Retold by L. L. Owens

Sir Arthur Conan Doyle

I called upon Sherlock Holmes. He was talking with a gentleman. The man had fiery red hair.

[2]"Welcome, my dear Dr. Watson," Holmes said.

[3]"This gentleman," Holmes explained to his guest, "has helped me with many cases."

[4]Holmes' guest, Mr. Wilson, greeted me politely.

[5]"Show Watson the newspaper ad," Holmes said to Wilson. "That will bring him up to speed."

[6]I took the *Morning Chronicle* from Wilson.

[7]The ad said, "TO ALL REDHEADED MEN: There is an open spot in the REDHEADED LEAGUE. Pay is 4 pounds a week. All REDHEADED men over 21 may apply. Come to the offices on Fleet Street. Monday—11:00 a.m."

[8]"What on earth?" I asked.

[9]"It is curious, isn't it?" Holmes chuckled. "Now, Mr. Wilson. Please tell your story. From the beginning."

[10]"I have a small business in the city," Wilson began. "I used to have two assistants. But now I can only keep one."

[11]"What is his name?" asked Holmes.

[12]"Vincent Spaulding," said Wilson. "He works hard. I am very lucky to have him. For he willingly works for half the regular pay. He has some odd habits though. He snaps pictures constantly. Then he dives into the cellar to develop them. He spends hours down there every day. Other than that, he's a good worker."

[13]"Go on," prompted Holmes.

[14]"Spaulding showed me this ad two months ago," Wilson continued. "That's when it ran. I thought it might be a joke. But he claimed he'd heard of the Redheaded League."

[15]"What did he know about it?" I asked.

[16]"He said it had been started by an American millionaire," Wilson explained. "The man had left money in his will. The money's purpose was to provide easy jobs for other redheads.

[17]"The pay wasn't great. But it would be extra since Spaulding could watch the store for me."

[18]"So you decided to check it out," prompted Holmes.

[19]"Yes," said Wilson. Then he described what he'd found.

[20]Apparently, swarms of redheaded men had flooded Fleet Street. They lined up around the block. But somehow, Spaulding pushed Wilson to the front. And they went into the office.

[21]A man with blazing red hair greeted them. He took one look at Wilson and shook his hand.

[22]"My name is Duncan Ross. And you meet every requirement," he said.

[23]Then, just to be sure, he tugged at Wilson's hair. "We have to be careful," he asserted. "We have twice been fooled by wigs. And once by paint! That settles it. You have won the position! When can you start?"

[24]"What are the hours? And what exactly is the job?" asked Wilson.

[25]"The hours are 10:00 a.m. to 2:00 p.m. The pay is four pounds per week. And the job is copying the Encyclopedia Britannica," said Ross.

[26]He went on. "You must stay in the office the whole time. If you leave, you lose your position."

[27]Wilson thought it sounded so easy! He said he could be ready the next morning.

[28]When Wilson arrived, everything was ready for him. Duncan Ross was there to start him off. He sat him at a table with pen and paper. And he gave him the first volume of the encyclopedia. Then he left.

[29]At the end of the day, he came back and checked on Wilson's progress. And he seemed quite pleased with his work.

[30]Wilson concluded his tale. "This went on day after day for eight weeks—until this morning. When I arrived, there was a note tacked to the door. I looked for Duncan Ross,

Sherlock Holmes studied the note.

this blunt announcement. Then we looked at Mr. Wilson's sad face. I regret to say that the two of us burst out laughing.

[33]"I see nothing funny about this!" cried our client.

[34]"No, no!" exclaimed Holmes. "I'm dreadfully sorry. We would love to take your case. It's just so unusual. But I assure you that we shall take the matter seriously. This is a seemingly harmless—and highly unusual—injustice. But that probably points to a larger misdeed. No doubt something criminal."

[35]"I thank you," said Wilson. "I do wish to get to the bottom of this awful prank."

[36]"I have one or two questions for you," said Holmes. "How long has your assistant been with you?"

[37]"About three months," replied Wilson.

[38]"Was he the only applicant?" Holmes asked.

[39]"No," Wilson said. "I had a dozen."

[40]"Why did you pick him?" I asked.

[41]"Because he was handy and would work cheaply," Wilson said.

[42]"Describe this Vincent Spaulding," directed Holmes. He was clearly intrigued.

but the landlord told me there was no such person. When I described Mr. Ross, the landlord knew him, but under a different name. He said that he'd paid his rent on the office and left this morning. With no forwarding address, of course."

[31]He showed us the note. It read, "To Mr. Jabez Wilson: The Redheaded League has dissolved. Please go home and don't come back!—October 9, 1890."

[32]Sherlock Holmes and I studied

Crime and Punishment

[43]"He's a small man," Wilson replied. "Very quick in his ways. He is over 30 but looks quite boyish. And he has a large white scar on his forehead."

[44]Holmes sat up in his chair. "I thought as much!" he cried. "That will do for now, Mr. Wilson. Today is Saturday. I hope that by Monday the case will be solved."

[45]Mr. Wilson showed himself out.

[46]Soon, we were in front of Mr. Wilson's shop. It was on the ground floor of his home. And it was closed for the weekend.

[47]Sherlock Holmes looked it over. Then he walked slowly up the street and back. He took note of the other houses.

[48]In front of Wilson's house, Holmes thumped the pavement with his walking stick. Then he knocked on the door. A bright-looking young fellow opened it. I knew he must be Wilson's assistant—Spaulding.

[49]Holmes said hello, then asked a question. "Could you tell me how to get to the St. James from here?"

[50]"Third right, fourth left," answered the assistant. And he promptly closed the door.

[51]"Smart fellow," observed Holmes as we walked away.

[52]"Evidently," I said, "you suspect him. Do you think he is behind the Redheaded League scam?"

[53]"I am quite sure of it," answered Holmes. "Did you notice the knees of his trousers?"

[54]"No," I said. "Are they important?"

[55]"Very," said Holmes. "They were ragged. As I suspected they would be. Now I'd like to explore the area."

[56]Behind Wilson's house was a row of businesses. Holmes took note of them all. There was Mortimer's and the newspaper shop. There was City Bank, the Vegetarian Restaurant, and the depot.

[57]"And now, Watson, we've done our work," said Holmes merrily. "It's time we had some play. Let's have a sandwich and a cup of coffee. Then it's off to the concert at the St. James."

[58]Later, we emerged from the St. James onto the busy street. We'd heard a lovely violin concert.

[59]"Meet me back at Baker Street. Tonight at ten," Holmes remarked.

[60]"Baker Street at ten," I promised.

[61]"There may be some danger," cautioned Holmes. "So bring your revolver."

[62] Holmes waved his hand and turned on his heel. Then he disappeared into the crowd.

[63] I arrived at my friend's room promptly at ten. Holmes was meeting with two men.

[64] "Watson!" he announced. "I think you know Mr. Jones—of Scotland Yard? Let me introduce you to Mr. Merryweather. He is the director of the City Bank."

[65] "How do you do," I nodded.

[66] "We're after John Clay," said Jones.

[67] "John Clay?" I asked. "The name rings a bell. But I cannot place it."

[68] "He's a murderer, a thief, a smasher, and a forger," said Jones. "I've been on his track for years."

[69] Holmes' eyes flashed. "We shall catch him tonight. It is past ten, gentlemen—quite time that we started."

[70] Holmes grabbed his coat and hat. Then he snatched his hunting crop from the corner. "One never knows," he remarked.

[71] We all took a carriage to Wilson's neighborhood. We were let out near the bank.

[72] Mr. Merryweather swiftly and quietly led us to the bank's cellar.

[73] Holmes fell to the floor at once.

With a lantern and a magnifying lens, he examined the cracks between the stones.

[74] "We have at least an hour before us," Holmes deduced. "For they won't take any steps until Wilson is safely in bed. Then they will not lose a minute."

[75] "What are they after?" I asked.

[76] "Our French gold," whispered Merryweather. "We have been storing a good deal of it these past three months. And we have received warnings that Clay might come after it."

[77] "Merryweather," whispered Holmes, "please put the screen over that lantern."

[78] "And sit in the dark?" asked Merryweather.

[79] "I am afraid so," said Holmes. "These are daring men. They may harm us unless we are careful. I shall stand behind this crate. And you conceal yourselves behind those. When I flash a light upon them, grab them. And Watson—if they fire, shoot them down."

[80] Holmes placed a screen over his lantern. This left us in pitch darkness.

[81] "They have but one way out," whispered Holmes. "That is back through Wilson's house into the

street. Did you do as I asked, Jones?"

[82]"Yes," Jones replied. "I have an inspector and two officers waiting at the front door."

[83]"Good," said Holmes. "Then we must be silent and wait."

[84]We waited for an hour and a quarter. But it seemed much longer. I was very tense. And all I could hear were the sounds of others breathing in the darkness.

[85]Suddenly, I saw a glimmer of light.

[86]At first, it was only a spark on the stone pavement. Then one of the broad, white stones turned over. It left a gaping hole through which streamed more light.

[87]A clean-cut, boyish face popped through the hole. He climbed through. Then he helped a companion do the same. His companion had a pale face and a shock of very red hair.

[88]"It's all clear," he whispered. "Have you the chisel? And the bags?"

[89]Sherlock Holmes seized the first intruder by the collar. The other dived back through the hole.

[90]The thief reached for a revolver. But Holmes slapped the man's wrist with his hunting crop. And the pistol clinked upon the stone floor.

[91]"It's no use, John Clay," said Holmes. "You have no chance at all."

[92]"So I see," Clay answered coolly. "I fancy that my pal is all right, though."

[93]"Wrong again!" Holmes exclaimed. "Three men are waiting for him at the door."

[94]"Then I must compliment you," said Clay.

[95]"And I you," Holmes allowed. "Your redheaded idea was very fresh. Very effective. But now you're off to the police station. Take him, Jones."

[96]"Thank you, Mr. Holmes!" cried Mr. Merryweather.

[97]"Not at all," replied the great detective.

[98]As usual, Holmes filled in the blanks over a late-night snack at Baker Street.

[99]"You see, Watson," he began, "it was obvious from the beginning."

[100]"Really!" I laughed.

[101]"Oh, quite," he said. "The Redheaded League was merely a cover. Someone wanted Mr. Wilson out of the way for several hours each day."

[102] "Clay no doubt thought of the scheme by chance. Probably when he noticed that Wilson's red hair matched his friend's," Holmes explained. "This happened after he had already been hired at Wilson's shop."

[103] "But how could you guess what the league was meant to cover?" I asked.

[104] "Wilson's business was small. So they didn't want to rob him," Holmes said. "It had to be, then, something out of the house. What could it be? Then I thought of the time the assistant spent in the cellar. And there was the end of this tangled clue."

[105] Holmes paced the floor as he told the rest of the story.

[106] "From Wilson's description, I knew his assistant wasn't really Vincent Spaulding. I knew he was the scoundrel John Clay. He is one of the smartest and most daring criminals in London. Think about it, Watson."

[107] "I am," I assured him. "But please do explain."

[108] "He was disappearing into the cellar for hours each day. For months on end. What was he doing?" Holmes wondered. "I could think of nothing. Except that he was digging a tunnel to some other building.

[109] "When we visited the scene, I beat upon the pavement. I was seeing whether Wilson's cellar stretched out in front or behind. This told me it was not in front."

[110] "And what about the young man's pants?" I asked. "Why were they important?"

[111] "I all but told you, old boy!" Holmes exclaimed. "The knees were worn and stained. Clearly, he spent hours working on his knees. The explanation, of course, is that he was digging. But for what?

[112] "So I walked around the corner. I saw that the City Bank building rested against our friend's shop. And I felt that I had solved the case.

[113] "When you left me, I called upon Jones at Scotland Yard. Then I called upon Mr. Merryweather."

[114] I was awed by his powers of deduction.

[115] "How did you know they would make their attempt tonight?" I asked.

[116] "Well, they had closed their Redheaded League offices. They no longer needed Wilson to stay away while they dug. That was a sign that they had finished their tunnel. But they had to use it soon. Robbing the

bank on Saturday would give them the weekend to escape. It was a gamble. But I felt sure that they would strike tonight."

[117]"You reasoned it out beautifully," I exclaimed. "As always."

[118]"It saves me from boredom," he answered, yawning. "I struggle to escape from boredom every day. These little mysteries help me do so."

[119]"Then it is a good arrangement," I said. "Your mysteries help you. And you help others."

[120]Holmes shrugged. "Well, perhaps it is of some little use. As someone once said—

[121]" 'A man's work is more important than the man himself!' "

If you have been timing your reading speed for this story, record your time below.

_____ : _____

Minutes   *Seconds*

UNDERSTANDING THE MAIN IDEA

The following questions will demonstrate your understanding of what the story is about, or the *main idea*. Choose the best answer for each question.

1. The story is mainly about

Ⓐ the Encyclopedia Britannica.

Ⓑ the capture of a master criminal.

Ⓒ a club for redheaded people.

Ⓓ the curse of having red hair.

2. The story could have been titled

Ⓐ "The Power of Deduction."

Ⓑ "Answering an Ad."

Ⓒ "The Curse of the Redheaded Man."

Ⓓ "How to Dig a Tunnel."

3. Which detail best supports the main idea of the story?

Ⓐ Dr. Watson helped Sherlock Holmes with many cases.

Ⓑ Jabez Wilson said he could be ready the next morning.

Ⓒ Holmes knew that the knees of Vincent Spaulding's trousers were a clue.

Ⓓ Holmes had a late-night snack at Baker Street.

4. Find another detail that supports the main idea. Write it on the lines below.

_____

_____

_____

RECALLING FACTS

The following questions will test how well you remember the facts in the story you just read. Choose the best answer for each question.

1. Jabez Wilson found out about the Redheaded League from

Ⓐ an American millionaire.

Ⓑ Holmes.

Ⓒ a fellow redhead.

Ⓓ Spaulding.

2. Jabez Wilson hired Vincent Spaulding mainly because

Ⓐ he worked cheaply.

Ⓑ he had red hair.

Ⓒ he was the only applicant.

Ⓓ he lived nearby.

3. On the lines below, write Jabez Wilson's job description at the Redheaded League, detailing his duties.

_____

_____

_____

_____

4. Sherlock Holmes thought he would catch his criminal at

Ⓐ the bank.

Ⓑ the newspaper office.

Ⓒ the Vegetarian Restaurant.

Ⓓ Scotland Yard.

An *inference* is a conclusion drawn from facts. A *generalization* is a general statement, idea, or rule that is supported by facts. Analyze the story by choosing the best answer to each question below.

1. What conclusion can you draw from paragraphs 20–29?

ⓐ Wilson would work for Duncan Ross for a long time.

ⓑ The job had odd requirements.

ⓒ The job was more difficult than it appeared to be.

ⓓ Wilson was hired because he had the most education.

2. What conclusion can you draw from paragraphs 46–51?

ⓐ Holmes thought Wilson's shop would be open.

ⓑ Holmes could not walk without his walking stick.

ⓒ Holmes was gathering clues to solve the mystery.

ⓓ Holmes didn't know his way around the city.

3. What generalization can be made from this story?

ⓐ All criminals eventually get caught.

ⓑ Some criminals can outsmart a detective.

ⓒ It is always easy to solve a mystery.

ⓓ Some criminals aren't as clever as they think.

4. It can be inferred from the story that

ⓐ Holmes was clever and observant.

ⓑ Holmes found solving crimes unrewarding.

ⓒ Holmes had a poor memory.

ⓓ Holmes paid little attention to details.

DETERMINING CAUSE AND EFFECT

Choose the best answers for the following questions to show the relationship between what happened in the story (*effects*) and why those things happened (*causes*).

1. Because Duncan Ross wanted to make sure Jabez Wilson really was a redhead, he

Ⓐ asked for a baby picture.

Ⓑ tugged at Wilson's hair.

Ⓒ gave Wilson a job.

Ⓓ sent Wilson to the end of the line.

2. What happened because John Clay saw that Jabez Wilson's red hair matched his friend's?

Ⓐ He called the Redheaded League immediately.

Ⓑ He tugged at Wilson's hair to make sure it was real.

Ⓒ He thought up the idea of the Redheaded League scam.

Ⓓ He asked for a job at Wilson's shop.

3. Why did John Clay and his companion dig a tunnel?

Ⓐ They were looking for a shortcut.

Ⓑ They wanted to investigate Wilson's shop.

Ⓒ They were curious about Wilson's cellar.

Ⓓ They were after the French gold stored at the City Bank.

4. Why was the Redheaded League dissolved?

Ⓐ Wilson had copied the entire encyclopedia.

Ⓑ The police had caught on to the criminals and closed the league.

Ⓒ The criminals wanted to steal money from Wilson's store.

Ⓓ The criminals had finished digging their tunnel.

USING CONTEXT CLUES

Skilled readers can often find the meaning of unfamiliar words by using *context clues*. This means they study the way the words are used in the text. Use the context clues in the excerpts below to determine the meaning of each **bold-faced** word. Then choose the answer that best matches the meaning of the word.

1. "Then he **snatched** his hunting crop from the corner."

   CLUE: "Holmes grabbed his coat and hat."

   Ⓐ mended
   Ⓑ caught
   Ⓒ grasped
   Ⓓ hid

2. " 'And you **conceal** yourselves behind those.' "

   CLUE: " 'I shall stand behind this crate.' "

   Ⓐ bury
   Ⓑ cover
   Ⓒ disguise
   Ⓓ hide

3. " 'The Redheaded League was merely a **cover**.' "

   CLUE: " 'Someone wanted Mr. Wilson out of the way for several hours each day.' "

   Ⓐ act
   Ⓑ blanket
   Ⓒ lid
   Ⓓ fact

4. " 'I knew he was the **scoundrel** John Clay.' "

   CLUE: " 'He is one of the smartest and most daring criminals in London.' "

   Ⓐ hero
   Ⓑ villain
   Ⓒ victim
   Ⓓ detective

The Cask of Amontillado

A story by Edgar Allan Poe

Retold by L. L. Owens

Edgar Allan Poe

Fortunato had insulted me. So I vowed revenge—not in so many words, of course, and never aloud.

2 So Fortunato had no reason to think that I meant him harm. I continued to smile whenever we met. He had no idea that I was smiling at the thought of his death.

3 I had given quite a bit of thought to finding Fortunato's weakness. It was hard, for he was well respected. And many feared him.

4 Then it hit me. Fortunato fancied himself a wine expert.

5 "That's it!" I cried. I was so delighted with my own genius. "It won't be long now!" I promised myself.

6 I planned a "chance meeting" with Fortunato. It was Carnival time, and I knew he would celebrate.

7 Saturday evening came. I dismissed my servants for the rest of the weekend. "Go!" I told them. "Have a good time at Carnival!"

8 When I found Fortunato, he wore a jester's costume. He was slightly tipsy from the wine he'd drunk at the festival.

9 "Hello there, good man!" he exclaimed. He was certainly glad to see me. There were bells on his pointed cap, and they jingled merrily as he shook my hand.

10 "Ah, Fortunato! Hello!" I acted surprised. "How lucky for me. I need some of your expert advice."

11 "How can I help, my friend?" he asked.

12 "I just bought a cask of Amontillado," I began. Then I paused to see whether I had his

attention. I did. This subject was dear to him.

[13]"Amontillado?" he urged. "Go on."

[14]So I continued. "Yes, Amontillado. I paid a nice price indeed. Now I fear that I have been tricked. It does not taste like Amontillado to me, at least not exactly. That's why I need your help. Someone with your knowledge can confirm my suspicions. Or you can make them go away."

[15]"I'll have to see for myself," Fortunato declared. "I doubt that anyone would have genuine Amontillado right now. Not during Carnival. Where are you keeping it?"

[16]"It's at home. In my vaults," I replied.

[17]"Let us go then."

[18]"That is very kind of you," I said. "But it is late, and you were on your way home. The wine will be there tomorrow. Besides, you are not dressed properly. It is cold, and the vaults are very damp. You'll be most uncomfortable."

[19]"Nonsense," he insisted. "The cold is of no consequence to me. Come! I want to taste that Amontillado!"

[20]Fortunato took my arm and turned us toward my estate. As we walked, I kept my cloak tightly closed. And I put on a black silk mask. "For the cold," I said to my good friend Fortunato.

[21]Once home, I offered Fortunato a torch. Then I led him down a long, winding staircase.

[22]"Do be careful," I said.

[23]"Don't worry about me," he replied. The bells on his cap jangled with each step.

[24]Finally, we reached the bottom. We had entered my family's catacombs. All the Montresors are buried there.

[25]Fortunato looked around. "Where is the cask?" he asked.

[26]"This way," I said. "Follow me."

[27]Then he began to cough. He choked and sputtered for several moments. When he caught his breath, I said, "Let's turn back. The dampness down here is making you ill."

[28]"Don't be ridiculous!" he replied. "I'm perfectly well. A bit of a cough won't kill me."

[29]"You're right. A cough won't kill you. Here, let me get you a drink." I pointed to a long rack of wine bottles. "A drop of this Medoc will warm us up. It will stave off your sickness too."

[30]I reached for a bottle and broke off its neck against the wall.

[31]"Drink this," I said.

[32]He took the bottle from my outstretched hand. Before sipping from it, he toasted, "To the dead that rest around us."

[33]"Here, here! To your long life," I replied, and I motioned for him to follow me.

[34]As we walked, he remarked, "These vaults are very large."

[35]"True. We Montresors were a great family."

[36]"Tell me—what is your coat of arms?"

[37]"A golden foot on a blue background. The foot is crushing a serpent."

[38]"And your motto?"

[39]"No one insults me without punishment," I replied.

[40]"A good one!" he said. The wine showed in his eyes. "And now, on to the Amontillado!"

[41]"On to the Amontillado!" I agreed.

[42]We continued our journey. We passed through generations of piled bones and under a series of low arches. Then we descended more stairs—two sets—until we arrived at a deep crypt. Three of its walls had been lined with human remains. They were piled high—all the way up to the vault overhead.

[43]The fourth wall had not been finished, or some of it had been knocked down. It is hard to say.

[44]"Here we are," I said cheerily. "The Amontillado is on the other side of this wall. It's in a special cask."

[45]Fortunato held his torch high. The flame was rather low in the dense air, so it was difficult for him to see what lay ahead.

[46]"Why did you choose to store it here?" he asked.

[47]The space was about three feet wide, four feet deep, and six feet high. It was backed by a wall of solid rock.

Montresor led Fortunato to his family's catacombs.

[48]"Go on in," I urged. "Amontillado—straight ahead!"

[49]He stepped over the low wall and into the small area. I followed on his heels. He reached the end of the space at once. He stood still for a moment, confused by the whole situation.

[50]In the blink of an eye, I had chained him to the wall!

[51]You see, there were two large iron staples in the rock. They were about two feet apart. From one staple hung a short chain. From the other hung a padlock. I worked swiftly. Fortunato was too stunned to resist.

[52]Once I'd locked him up, I stepped back over the wall.

[53]"I offered to let you turn around," I said, shrugging. "Let me offer again. What's that? No? Then I shall be forced to leave you."

[54]"But—but—the Amontillado!" cried my friend. "Montresor—the Amontillado!" He was still in shock.

[55]"Indeed!" I said. "The Amontillado!"

[56]With that, I produced a trowel from under my cloak. Then I found my stash of supplies—building stone, mortar, and so on. Hastily, I began to wall up the entrance to the space.

[57]I soon realized that the effects of the wine Fortunato had drunk had worn off. He moaned, "I do not understand. I do not understand."

[58]Then he grew silent. This lasted for quite some time.

[59]I worked hard. Soon, I had laid the third row, then the fourth.

[60]Fortunato tried to break free. He shook his chains mightily for several minutes. I wanted to enjoy the spectacle, so I stopped my work and sat down upon the bones for a bit.

[61]My dear friend tired and quieted himself. And I resumed my work. I completed the next three rows—up to my chest—with vigor. Again, I paused. I stuck my torch over the wall to have a look.

[62]Suddenly, Fortunato let loose with several loud, forceful, mad screams. I took a step back. I even trembled.

[63]But then I realized that Fortunato could do me no harm. Not from his position! So I went back to work. I matched his screams in volume and strength until he grew still.

[64]Midnight—and my task was nearly complete. I had finished three more rows. There was just one more to go.

[65]I fitted the final stone. As I prepared to plaster it, a low laugh rose up from behind the fresh wall. The hairs on the back of my neck stood up at the sound of it.

[66]The sad voice that called out baffled me. Surely, this cannot be the voice of the strong, noble Fortunato. The voice said—

[67]"Ha! ha! ha! Hee! hee! hee! What a very good joke indeed. An excellent jest, Montresor. We'll laugh about this later. Ho! ho! ho! Oh, yes. We will enjoy this story for years to come. We can tell it to our wives over some wine."

[68]"Perhaps some Amontillado!" I taunted.

[69]"Ho! ho! ho! Yes, of course! Amontillado! But now, we must hurry. Will they not be waiting for us—the Lady Fortunato and the rest? Come now. Let us be gone."

[70]"Yes," I said. "Let us be gone!"

[71]"For the love of God, Montresor!"

[72]"Yes," I said. "For the love of God!"

[73]This time, Fortunato did not reply. I grew restless. I called out. "Fortunato!"

[74]Still, nothing. Again I called. "Fortunato!"

[75]I thrust my torch through the small hole that remained. I let it drop. A jingling of the jester's bells was the only response.

[76]My heart grew sick. The dampness of the catacombs was getting to me.

[77]With renewed energy, I forced the last stone into place. I plastered it up. The mortar would dry in time. Then I piled my ancestral bones high in front of the new wall. And for half of a century, no mortal has disturbed them.

[78]May he rest in peace!

If you have been timing your reading speed for this story, record your time below.

—————— : ——————

Minutes   *Seconds*

UNDERSTANDING THE MAIN IDEA

The following questions will demonstrate your understanding of what the story is about, or the *main idea*. Choose the best answer for each question.

1. This story is mainly about

Ⓐ a coat of arms.

Ⓑ a man's revenge.

Ⓒ a celebration.

Ⓓ a cask of wine.

2. The story could have been titled

Ⓐ "Montresor's Estate."

Ⓑ "The Carnival Season."

Ⓒ "Getting Even."

Ⓓ "For the Love of Wine."

3. Which detail best supports the main idea of the story?

Ⓐ It was the Carnival season.

Ⓑ There were bells on Fortunato's pointed cap.

Ⓒ All the Montresors were buried in the catacombs.

Ⓓ Montresor led Fortunato to a crypt.

4. Find another detail that supports the main idea. Write it on the lines below.

_____

_____

_____

_____

RECALLING FACTS

The following questions will test how well you remember the facts in the story you just read. Choose the best answer for each question.

1. Montresor figured out that Fortunato's weakness was that he

Ⓐ feared everyone he met.

Ⓑ could not hurt a person's feelings.

Ⓒ thought he was an expert on wines.

Ⓓ felt inferior to Montresor.

2. Montresor's family motto was

Ⓐ "Love will conquer all."

Ⓑ "Long live the Montresors."

Ⓒ "Kindness is always rewarded."

Ⓓ "No one insults me without punishment."

3. To make Fortunato unaware of the trap he had set, Montresor

Ⓐ blindfolded Fortunato.

Ⓑ tried to discourage Fortunato from continuing down because of the dampness.

Ⓒ dressed up like a jester.

Ⓓ didn't speak to Fortunato the whole time they were climbing down into the vaults.

4. The story took place mainly

Ⓐ in the vaults.

Ⓑ in a vineyard.

Ⓒ at the Carnival.

Ⓓ in Montresor's living room.

READING BETWEEN THE LINES

An *inference* is a conclusion drawn from facts. A *generalization* is a general statement, idea, or rule that is supported by facts. Analyze the story by choosing the best answer to each question below.

1. **What conclusion can you draw from paragraph 20?**

   Ⓐ Montresor was in costume for the Carnival.

   Ⓑ Montresor wanted to be unrecognizable.

   Ⓒ Montresor wanted to put Fortunato at ease.

   Ⓓ Montresor didn't want to get sick from the cold.

2. **What conclusion can you draw from paragraphs 27–40?**

   Ⓐ Montresor was genuinely concerned about Fortunato.

   Ⓑ Montresor's family wasn't really buried in the vaults.

   Ⓒ Fortunato didn't read between the lines of what Montresor was saying.

   Ⓓ Fortunato had a feeling something bad was about to happen to him.

3. **What generalization can you make from the story?**

   Ⓐ Some people are able to conceal their true feelings well.

   Ⓑ A vengeful person can never hide his or her feelings.

   Ⓒ All acts of revenge fail in the end.

   Ⓓ Every act of revenge is violent.

4. **It can be inferred that the story takes place in**

   Ⓐ spring.

   Ⓑ summer.

   Ⓒ winter.

   Ⓓ autumn.

Crime and Punishment

DETERMINING CAUSE AND EFFECT

Choose the best answers for the following questions to show the relationship between what happened in the story (*effects*) and why those things happened (*causes*).

1. On the lines below, write the cause and effect of Montresor's plan.

_____

_____

_____

_____

2. What happened because Montresor asked for Fortunato's help identifying a wine?

Ⓐ Fortunato went to the Carnival.

Ⓑ Fortunato insulted Montresor.

Ⓒ Fortunato thought he was a wine expert.

Ⓓ Fortunato entered the vaults with Montresor.

3. Why did Montresor dislike Fortunato?

Ⓐ Fortunato had cheated Montresor out of money.

Ⓑ Fortunato had earned a higher social rank than Montresor.

Ⓒ Fortunato had insulted Montresor.

Ⓓ Fortunato had replaced Montresor as chief wine expert.

4. Why did Montresor dismiss his servants?

Ⓐ He wanted them to enjoy the Carnival.

Ⓑ He always gave them the weekends off.

Ⓒ He didn't need their services that night.

Ⓓ He wanted to be alone with Fortunato.

———— ■ ————

USING CONTEXT CLUES

Skilled readers can often find the meaning of unfamiliar words by using *context clues*. This means they study the way the words are used in the text. Use the context clues in the excerpts below to determine the meaning of each **bold-faced** word. Then choose the answer that best matches the meaning of the word.

1. "We had entered my family's **catacombs**."

CLUE: "All the Montresors are buried there."

   Ⓐ rooms

   Ⓑ vaults

   Ⓒ galleries

   Ⓓ hallways

2. " 'It will **stave off** your sickness too.' "

CLUE: " 'A drop of this Medoc will warm us up.' . . . 'To your long life,' I replied . . ."

   Ⓐ reject

   Ⓑ add to

   Ⓒ punish

   Ⓓ prevent

3. "I wanted to enjoy the **spectacle**."

CLUE: "Fortunato tried to break free. He shook his chains mightily for several minutes."

   Ⓐ sight

   Ⓑ celebration

   Ⓒ story

   Ⓓ discovery

4. "The sad voice that called out **baffled** me."

CLUE: "Surely, this cannot be the voice of the strong, noble Fortunato."

   Ⓐ frightened

   Ⓑ confused

   Ⓒ discouraged

   Ⓓ frustrated

The Lady, or the Tiger?

A story by Frank R. Stockton

Retold by Paula Reece

Frank R. Stockton

In the very olden time there lived a king. This spirited king had a cruel streak. And he had some crazy ideas. But his people obeyed him so much that his ideas usually became facts.

[2]He usually discussed things with the person he trusted the most—himself. And when he and himself agreed upon anything, the thing was done.

[3]When everything went smoothly, the king was composed and happy. And whenever there was a little hitch, he was even more composed and happier yet. For nothing pleased him more than to make the crooked straight or to crush down uneven places.

[4]One of his borrowed ideas was that of a public arena. The arena displayed manly and beastly bravery.

This caused his citizens' minds to be refined and cultured.

[5]But even here the king showed his enthusiastic and cruel side. He used the huge stadium for true justice. Crime was punished or innocence rewarded by the laws of something fair and flawless—chance.

[6]If a citizen was accused of a crime, the king decided if it interested him. If it did, then the public was notified. On a certain day the fate of the person would be decided in the king's arena.

[7]On that day all the people gathered in the bleachers. The king would be surrounded by his court. He would sit high on his throne on one side of the arena.

[8]When the king gave a signal, a door beneath him opened. The accused person stepped out into the

arena. Directly across from the accused were two doors. They were exactly alike and side-by-side. The person on trial had to walk straight to the doors and open one of them.

[9]The person could open either door. But he could receive no help or opinions except from chance itself.

[10]If the accused opened one door, out came a hungry tiger. It would be the fiercest and cruelest that could be captured. It would immediately spring upon him and tear him to pieces. It was a punishment for his guilt.

[11]As soon as the case of the criminal was decided, sad iron bells were clanged in the kingdom. Great cries went up from the hired mourners who were posted on the outer rim of the arena. Then the large audience went slowly home with bowed heads and heavy hearts. They mourned that one so young and fair, or so old and respected, should have deserved such a frightful fate.

[12]But if the accused person opened the other door, out came a lady. She was the most suitable to his age and rank that His Majesty could select among his citizens. And to this lady the accused was instantly married. It was a reward of his innocence.

[13]It didn't matter if he already had a wife and family. Or if he was already engaged to a woman of his own choosing. The king didn't allow such arrangements to interfere with his great scheme of punishment and reward.

[14]The vows took place right away in the arena. Another door opened beneath the king. A priest was followed by a band of singers and dancing maidens blowing golden horns. They went to where the pair stood. Then the wedding was promptly and cheerily performed.

[15]Following the ceremony, merry brass bells rang. The people shouted glad hurrahs. The innocent man, followed by children dropping flowers on his path, led his bride to his home.

[16]This was the king's semicruel method of carrying out justice. Its perfect fairness is clear. The criminal could not know out of which door would come the lady. He opened either door he wished. And he never had the slightest idea whether, in the next instant, he would be devoured or married.

[17]Sometimes the tiger came out of one door. Sometimes it came out of the other. The decisions were not only fair, they were positively final.

The accused person never knew whether or not a tiger would spring from behind the chosen door.

The accused person was instantly punished if he found himself guilty. And if innocent, he was rewarded on the spot—whether he liked it or not. There was no escape from the judgments of the king's arena.

[18]The trials were very popular. Many people gathered. And they never knew whether they would witness a bloody slaughter or a cheery wedding. The uncertainty made it more appealing.

[19]So the people were entertained and pleased. And the concerned citizens couldn't bring any charge of unfairness against the plan. Because didn't the accused person have the whole matter in his own hands?

[20]Now this semicruel king had a daughter. She was as blooming as his most elaborate ideas. And she had a soul as passionate and commanding as his own. She was the apple of her father's eye. And he loved her more than anything.

[21]One of the king's attendants was a young man. He was a fine man but had a low rank, just like many of the heroes of romance who loved royal maidens.

[22]And this royal maiden loved her hero. He was more handsome and braver than any other man in the kingdom. And she was completely devoted to him.

[23]This love affair moved along happily for many months. Until one day the king found out about it. He did not hesitate in regard to his duty. The young man was promptly thrown into prison. And a day was chosen for his trial in the king's arena.

[24]This, of course, was an especially important occasion. His Majesty and the people were greatly interested in the trial. Never before had there been such a case. Never before had a citizen dared to love the daughter of a king.

[25]The tiger cages of the kingdom were searched for the most savage beast. The fiercest monster would be selected for the arena.

[26]All of the young, beautiful maidens in the kingdom were carefully examined by worthy judges. That was so the young man would have a fitting bride—just in case fate did not determine for him a different future.

[27]Of course, everybody knew that the deed with which the man was charged had been done. He had loved the princess. And neither he, she, nor anyone else thought of denying it.

[28]But the king would not allow any fact of this kind to interfere with the workings of his court of judgment, especially when he took such delight in it. No matter how it turned out, the young man would be out of his daughter's life. And the king would enjoy watching the turn of events. Those events would determine whether the young man had done wrong in loving the princess.

[29]The appointed day arrived. The people gathered from far and near. They crowded the bleachers of the arena. Those unable to get in massed themselves against its outside walls. The king and his court were in their places, opposite the fateful twin doors.

[30]All was ready. The signal was given. A door beneath the king opened. The lover of the princess walked into the arena. He was tall and beautiful.

[31]A low hum sounded throughout the crowd. Most of the audience had not known that so grand a young man lived among them. No wonder the princess loved him! What a terrible thing for him to be there!

[32]The young man went farther into the arena. Then he turned to bow to the king. It was the custom. But the young man was not thinking at all of the king. His eyes were fixed upon the princess. She sat to the right of her father.

[33]From the moment she heard about her lover's trial, the princess had thought of nothing else, night or day. She had more power, influence, and forcefulness than anyone who had ever before been interested in such a case. So she did what no other person had done—she found out the secret of the doors. She knew behind which door waited the tiger. And she knew behind which door stood the lady.

[34]The doors were thick with heavy curtains on the inside. So it

Crime and Punishment

was impossible that any noise would come from within. Nothing would give a person an idea of what was inside. But gold and the power of a woman's will brought the secret to the princess.

[35] She not only knew behind which door stood the lady. She also knew who the lady was. She was one of the loveliest damsels of the king's court. She had been selected as the reward of the accused if he was proven innocent of his crime. The princess hated her.

[36] The princess had often seen, or imagined she saw, this lovely damsel glancing at her lover. Flirting, she thought. And sometimes the princess thought that her lover had not only noticed, but returned the glances.

[37] Now and then she had seen them talking together. It was only for a moment or two. But a lot can be said in a short time. It could have been about the most unimportant topics. But how could she know that?

[38] The young man turned and looked at the princess. His eyes met hers. She was paler than anyone in the vast ocean of faces around her. But he could tell by her face that she knew.

[39] He had expected her to know it. He understood her nature. He knew that she would never rest until she discovered the secret.

[40] His quick and anxious glance asked, "Which one?" It was as plain to her as if he shouted it from where he stood. There was not an instant to be lost. The question was asked in a flash. It must be answered in another.

[41] Her right arm lay on the cushioned armrest.

[42] She raised her hand. She made a slight, quick movement to the right. No one but her lover saw her.

[43] He turned. Then he quickly walked across the empty space. Every heart stopped beating. Every breath was held. Every eye was fixed on the man. Without hesitating, he went to the door on the right and opened it.

[44] Now to the point of the story. Did the tiger come out of that door? Or did the lady?

[45] The more we think about this question, the harder it is to answer. It involves a study of the human heart, which leads us through mazes of passion. It is often difficult to find our way out of such mazes.

[46] Don't think of what you would do. Think of what the hotblooded princess would have done. Despair and jealousy combined to torment

her soul. She had lost her lover, but who should then have him?

[47]So often had she thought in horror of her lover opening the door behind which waited the cruel fangs of the tiger. But how much more often had she seen him at the other door! In her daydreams she had ground her teeth and torn her hair when she saw his face in ecstasy as he opened the door of the lady!

[48]Her soul had burned in agony when she had seen him rush to meet that woman. When she had heard the glad shouts from the crowd and the wild ringing of the happy bells. When she had seen the priest advance to the couple. And make them man and wife before her very eyes!

[49]Wouldn't it be better for him to die at once? Then he could wait for the princess in paradise.

[50]And yet, that awful tiger! Those shrieks! The blood!

[51]Her decision had been shown in an instant. But it had been made after days and nights of terrible consideration. She had known she would be asked. She had decided what she would answer. And without any hesitation, she had moved her hand to the right.

[52]Which came out of the opened door—the lady, or the tiger?

If you have been timing your reading speed for this story, record your time below.

_____ : _____

Minutes   **Seconds**

Crime and Punishment

UNDERSTANDING THE MAIN IDEA

The following questions will demonstrate your understanding of what the story is about, or the *main idea*. Choose the best answer for each question.

1. This story is mainly about

Ⓐ a crowd's reaction to a trial.

Ⓑ a princess.

Ⓒ a king's system of justice.

Ⓓ a hungry tiger.

2. The story could have been titled

Ⓐ "The History of Arenas."

Ⓑ "A Telling Decision."

Ⓒ "The Eye of the Tiger."

Ⓓ "Olden Times."

3. Which detail supports the main idea of this story?

Ⓐ The king was anxious to use his system of justice on the young man.

Ⓑ One of the king's attendants was a young man.

Ⓒ The love affair moved along happily for many months.

Ⓓ The princess had seen her lover and the lovely damsel talking together.

4. Find another detail that supports the main idea of this story. Write it on the lines below.

_____

_____

_____

_____

RECALLING FACTS

The following questions will test how well you remember the facts in the story you just read. Choose the best answer for each question.

1. The king was happiest when

Ⓐ he didn't have any problems to deal with.

Ⓑ he spent time with his daughter.

Ⓒ his people obeyed him without question.

Ⓓ he could punish a criminal.

2. The king discussed important matters with

Ⓐ his daughter.

Ⓑ himself.

Ⓒ his tiger.

Ⓓ his court.

3. When it was time to choose the door, the young man looked for help from

Ⓐ the king.

Ⓑ the court.

Ⓒ the princess.

Ⓓ the audience.

4. When the king learned about the princess and her lover, he immediately

Ⓐ punished the princess.

Ⓑ exiled the man from the kingdom.

Ⓒ called for the priest to marry them.

Ⓓ threw the man into prison.

An *inference* is a conclusion drawn from facts. A *generalization* is a general statement, idea, or rule that is supported by facts. Analyze the story by choosing the best answer to each question below.

1. What conclusion can you draw from paragraphs 21–23?

Ⓐ The king wanted the princess to marry someone noble.

Ⓑ The king respected his daughter's decisions.

Ⓒ The young man was courting the princess against her will.

Ⓓ The king wanted the princess to marry someone from a lower class.

2. On the lines below, write a conclusion for paragraphs 34–37.

_____

_____

_____

_____

3. What generalization can you make from this story?

Ⓐ A person is always innocent until proven guilty.

Ⓑ Justice is never served.

Ⓒ Innocent people are sometimes punished.

Ⓓ All systems of justice are perfect.

4. It can be inferred from the story that the

Ⓐ young man completely trusted the princess.

Ⓑ princess completely trusted the young man.

Ⓒ princess did not have a jealous bone in her body.

Ⓓ princess desperately wanted her lover to live.

DETERMINING CAUSE AND EFFECT

Choose the best answers for the following questions to show the relationship between what happened in the story (*effects*) and why those things happened (*causes*).

1. **Because the princess had learned of her lover's trial, she**

   Ⓐ asked her father for his blessing.

   Ⓑ used her power to learn the secret of the doors.

   Ⓒ ran away and refused to return until her lover was released.

   Ⓓ developed a friendship with the young maiden who was to be his reward.

2. **What happened because the young man was unsure about which door to open?**

   Ⓐ He looked to the audience for a signal.

   Ⓑ He looked to the king for a signal.

   Ⓒ He looked to the princess for a signal.

   Ⓓ He made his own decision.

3. **Why did the citizens attend the trials?**

   Ⓐ They tried to help the accused people choose the correct door.

   Ⓑ They liked to throw fruit at the accused.

   Ⓒ They were forced to attend by the king.

   Ⓓ They were entertained by the uncertainty of the outcomes.

4. **Why did a low hum sound through the crowd when the young man stepped into the arena?**

   Ⓐ The citizens thought the young man looked guilty.

   Ⓑ The citizens didn't know such a grand young man lived among them.

   Ⓒ The citizens were trying to distract the young man.

   Ⓓ The citizens were trying to think of a way to help the young man escape.

USING CONTEXT CLUES

Skilled readers can often find the meaning of unfamiliar words by using *context clues*. This means they study the way the words are used in the text. Use the context clues in the excerpts below to determine the meaning of each **bold-faced** word. Then choose the answer that best matches the meaning of the word.

1. "They **mourned** that one so young and fair, or so old and respected, should have deserved such a frightful fate."

CLUE: "Then the large audience went slowly home with bowed heads and heavy hearts."

    Ⓐ decided

    Ⓑ believed

    Ⓒ grieved

    Ⓓ rejoiced

2. "The **uncertainty** made it more appealing."

CLUE: "And they never knew whether they would witness a bloody slaughter or a cheery wedding."

    Ⓐ concern

    Ⓑ suspense

    Ⓒ mistrust

    Ⓓ suspicion

3. "The tiger cages of the kingdom were searched for the most **savage** beast."

CLUE: "The fiercest monster would be selected for the arena."

    Ⓐ vicious

    Ⓑ unusual

    Ⓒ wolfish

    Ⓓ reckless

4. "[The king] did not **hesitate** in regard to his duty."

CLUE: "The young man was promptly thrown into prison."

    Ⓐ stall

    Ⓑ proceed

    Ⓒ see

    Ⓓ act

The Invisible Man

A story by G. K. Chesterton

Retold by Paula Reece

G. K. Chesterton

O ne shop in Camden Town stood out from the rest. For in the window shone different colored lights. They were broken up by many mirrors. This made the brilliant lights dance on the brightly colored cakes and sweets that were displayed.

2 Young children were attracted to this window. But a young man, not less than 24, was staring into the same shop window. To him, also, the shop had a fiery charm. But it wasn't just because of the chocolates.

3 His name was John Turnbull Angus. He was a tall, burly young man with red hair. His face was determined.

4 He entered the shop at last. But he walked through the shop to the back room. It was a sort of pastry restaurant. He raised his hat to the young lady who was serving.

5 Laura Hope was an elegant, alert girl. Her face was flushed, and she had quick, dark eyes. After a few moments, she went to the man to take his order.

6 It was obvious that he had ordered there before. "I want, please," he said with precision, "one cinnamon bun and a small cup of black coffee." Then, an instant before the girl could turn away, he added, "Also, I want you to marry me."

7 The young lady suddenly stiffened. "I don't allow those kind of jokes," she said.

8 The red-haired young man lifted his eyes. "Really and truly," he said, "I am serious."

9 The young lady stared at him. She seemed to show the shadow of

a smile. Then she turned and walked to a window in the back room.

[10]At last she swung around again. She returned to Mr. Angus and sat down. She didn't look at him unfavorably. But she did look at him with complete agitation.

[11]"You don't give me much time to think," she said.

[12]"I'm not such a fool," he answered.

[13]"Mr. Angus," she said, "before there is a minute more of this nonsense, I must tell you something."

[14]"Be my guest," Mr. Angus said.

[15]"I must first tell you that my father owned the inn called the Red Fish at Ludbury," she said. "I used to serve people in the bar.

[16]"Once in a while travelers came to the Red Fish," she continued. "There were two men who came in a lot. I felt sorry for them. They were both odd. One of them was a very small man, something like a dwarf. He was very clever at things that could never be of any use. Like making 15 matches set fire to each other like a firework. Or cutting a banana into a dancing doll. His name was Isidore Smythe."

[17]"What about the other man?" Angus asked.

[18]"Yes, him," Miss Hope said. "He was more silent and ordinary. But somehow he alarmed me much more than poor little Smythe. He was very tall and lean. And he had one of the most awful squints I have ever seen. His name was James Welkin. I figure this horrible squint made him bitter."

[19]"So, what happened?" asked Angus.

[20]"Well, I was really puzzled and sorry when both men offered to marry me in the same week," she said.

[21]"What did you do?" Angus asked.

[22]"Well, I didn't want them to know the real reason I wouldn't marry them," Miss Hope said. "Which was that they were so ugly. So I made up another excuse. I said that I would not marry anyone unless he had made a life for himself. They were just living on money they had inherited."

[23]"How did they take it?" Angus asked.

[24]"Two days after I had told them this, the whole trouble began," she said. "I heard that both of them had gone off to seek their fortunes. Like they were in some sort of silly fairy tale."

[25]"Have you seen them since?" asked Angus.

[26]"No," Miss Hope answered, "but I've gotten two letters from Smythe. I suppose you've heard of 'Smythe's Silent Service'?" she said. "Everyone's heard of it. It's a clockwork invention for doing all the housework by machinery. You know the slogan, 'Press a Button—Ten Housemaids Who Never Flirt.' They are making loads of money.

[27]"Anyway," she continued, "I am terrified that Smythe will turn up any minute. I'm scared he'll tell me he's carved his way in the world—which he certainly has."

[28]"What about the other man?" Angus asked.

[29]Laura Hope got to her feet suddenly. "I haven't seen him, and he hasn't written to me. But I am frightened of him. And he has driven me mad. For I have felt him where he couldn't have been. And I have heard his voice when he couldn't have spoken."

[30]"Well, my dear," said the young man, "when did you think you felt and heard our squinting friend?"

[31]"I heard James Welkin laugh as plainly as I hear you speak," said the girl. "There was nobody there. For I stood just outside the shop at the corner. And I could see down both streets at once. I had not thought of him in nearly a year. But a few seconds later the first letter came from Mr. Smythe."

[32]"Did you ever hear the voice speak?" asked Angus.

[33]Laura shuddered. Then she said, "Yes. Just when I had finished reading the second letter from Mr. Smythe. Just then I heard Welkin say, 'He can't have you, though.' It was as plain as if he were in the room. I think I must be crazy."

[34]Just then a small car zoomed up to the door of the shop and stopped. In the same flash of time, a small man in a shiny top hat stood in the outer room.

[35]Angus walked up to the newcomer. Just a glance told Angus that this man was in love. Angus knew it had to be Isidore Smythe.

[36]"Has Miss Hope seen that thing on the window?" Smythe asked.

[37]"On the window?" asked Angus.

[38]"There's no time to explain," the small millionaire said. "There's something going on here that has to be investigated."

[39]Smythe pointed his polished walking stick at the window. Angus couldn't believe his eyes. Along the front of the glass, a long strip of paper was pasted. It hadn't been there when he looked through it before.

[40]It was a yard and a half or so of stamp paper. And it was gummed to the outside of the glass. On it was scrawled, "If you marry Smythe, he will die."

[41]"Laura," said Angus, "you're not crazy."

[42]"It's that fellow, Welkin," said Smythe. "I've been getting threatening letters from him at my apartment. I can't even find out who leaves them. The doorman of the building swears that no suspicious characters have been seen."

[43]"Well, the man cannot be very far off," said Angus. "But he's probably too far off to be chased. I know a very clever man who could help you."

[44]"Who is that?" Smythe asked.

[45]"His name is Flambeau," said Angus. "His brains are worth money. He lives in Village Apartments."

[46]"I live in Grand Apartments," said Smythe. "It's right around the corner. Maybe you could come with me to my house first. I can give you Welkin's letters. Then you can go get your friend the detective."

[47]Both men said a sort of formal farewell to Miss Hope. Then they took off in Smythe's little car.

[48]When they sped around the corner toward the apartment building, they passed a man selling chestnuts. Then they saw a policeman walking slowly.

[49]As soon as the car pulled in front of the apartments, Smythe jumped out. He started questioning a tall security guard and a short doorman. He asked whether anyone or anything had gone to his apartment.

[50]The men told Smythe that nobody and nothing had passed them since he had left. Then Angus and Smythe jumped into the elevator and rocketed up to the top floor.

[51]Smythe opened the door to his apartment. In the entryway stood rows of half-human mechanical figures. They were headless and had two great hooks like arms for carrying trays.

[52]But it wasn't the robots the men were staring at. Between the two rows of the domestic dummies lay something more interesting. It was a white, tattered scrap of paper. It was scrawled with red ink that was not yet dry.

[53]Smythe handed it to Angus without a word. Angus read, "If you have been to see her today, I shall kill you."

[54]There was a short silence. Then Isidore Smythe said, "Would you like

Crime and Punishment

a little drink? I rather feel as if I should."

[55]"Thank you," said Angus, "but I should like a little Flambeau. I'm going to fetch him at once."

[56]"Right you are," said Smythe. "Bring him here as fast as you can."

[57]As Angus was walking down the steps, he saw the doorman. He made him promise to remain there until Angus returned with the detective. He was to keep any sort of stranger from coming up the stairs.

[58]The security guard made a similar promise at the front door. Angus learned that there was no back door.

[59]Then Angus saw the policeman. He convinced him to stand opposite the entrance and watch it. And finally he promised to pay the man selling chestnuts if he waited there until Angus returned. He was then to tell him whether any man, woman, or child had gone into the building.

[60]"I've made a ring around the building, anyhow," said Angus as he walked away. "They can't all four of them be Mr. Welkin's partners."

[61]Angus reached Village Apartments. Flambeau greeted him in a den behind his office. In it were swords, strange items from the Far East, native cooking pots, a soft

Angus accompanied Smythe to his apartment.

Persian cat, and a small dusty-looking Roman Catholic priest, who looked rather out of place.

[62]"This is my friend, Father Brown," said Flambeau.

[63]"Well," said Angus, "I'm afraid I've come on business." Angus began to tell the story.

[64]Flambeau grew more and more concerned. But the little priest

seemed to be left out of it. Soon Flambeau said, "I think you had better tell me the rest on the road. I don't think we have any time to lose."

[65]"Yes," said Angus, "though he's safe enough for now. I've set four men to watch the only entrance."

[66]They set out for the street. The priest followed behind.

[67]They first met the chestnut seller. He swore stubbornly that he had watched the door. And he had seen no visitor enter.

[68]The policeman was even more firm. He said he had experience with crooks of all kinds. He wasn't so foolish as to expect suspicious characters to look suspicious. He looked out for anybody. "And, so help me," he said, "there's been nobody."

[69]"I've got the right to ask any man, whether he's a duke or a garbage man, what he wants in this building," said the security guard. "And I'll swear that there's been nobody to ask since this gentleman went away."

[70]Father Brown was standing back. He looked at the pavement. Then he said modestly, "Has nobody been up and down the stairs, then, since the snow began to fall? It began while we were at Flambeau's."

[71]"Nobody's been in here, sir," said the man. "You can take it from me."

[72]"Then I wonder what that is," said the priest. He was staring at the ground.

[73]The others also looked down. They gasped. For down the middle of the entrance ran a stringy pattern of gray footprints stamped upon the white snow.

[74]"I don't believe it!" cried Angus. "It's the Invisible Man!"

[75]He dashed up the stairs without another word. Flambeau followed. But Father Brown just looked around the streets as if he had lost interest.

[76]When they entered the apartment, they didn't see anyone. But there was something in the middle of the dummies. Right where the piece of paper with the red ink had been. It looked like red ink had spilled out of its bottle. But it wasn't red ink.

[77]Flambeau cried, "Murder!" He explored every corner and cupboard of the apartment in five minutes. But Isidore Smythe was not in the place, either dead or alive.

[78]"My friend," said Flambeau, "not only is your murderer invisible, but so is the murdered man! I must go down and talk to Father Brown."

[79]They passed the doorman on the way down the stairs. He swore that he had not let a trespasser by.

[80]"Where is the policeman?" Angus asked when they returned to Father Brown outside.

[81]"I sent him down the road to check out something," said Father Brown.

[82]Just then the policeman came running up to the crowd. He went straight to Father Brown. "You're right, sir," he said. "They've just found poor Mr. Smythe's body in the canal down below."

[83]Angus was very confused. "Did he run down and drown himself?" he asked.

[84]"He never came down, I swear," said the policeman. "And he wasn't drowned either. He died of a stab wound to the heart."

[85]"And yet you saw no one enter?" asked Flambeau. He was completely baffled.

[86]"Let's walk down the road a little," said Father Brown.

[87]So Flambeau and Angus followed Father Brown. As they reached the end of the street, Father Brown said suddenly, "Stupid of me! I forgot to ask the policeman something. I wonder if they found a light brown sack."

[88]"Why a light brown sack?" asked Angus, bewildered.

[89]"Because if it was any other colored sack, the case must begin over again," said Father Brown. "But if it was a light brown sack, why, the case is finished."

[90]"You must tell us what you are talking about," said Flambeau.

[91]They continued walking. Father Brown said, "Have you ever noticed that people never answer what you say? They answer what you mean, or what they think you mean."

[92]"What do you mean?" asked Angus.

[93]"Suppose one lady says to another in a boardinghouse, 'Is anybody staying with you?' " said Father Brown. "The lady doesn't answer, 'Yes, the butler, the maid, and so on.' Even though the maid may be in the room or the butler behind her chair. She says, 'There is nobody staying with us.' She means nobody of the sort you mean."

[94]"Go on," said Flambeau.

[95]"But suppose there is a disease outbreak," the priest continued. "A doctor asks, 'Who is staying in the house?' Then the lady will remember the butler, the maid, and the rest."

[96]"What does this have to do with the murder?" asked Angus.

[97]"Those four quite honest men said that no man had gone into the building. But they did not really mean that no man had gone into it. They meant that no man whom they could suspect of being the murderer. A man did go into the house and did come out of it. But they never noticed him."

[98]"An invisible man?" asked Angus.

[99]"A mentally invisible man," said Father Brown. "Of course you can't think of such a man until you do think of him. That's why he's so clever. I began to think of him through a couple of things in the tale Mr. Angus told us."

[100]"What was that?" asked Angus.

[101]"First of all there was the huge amount of stamp paper on the window," said Father Brown. "Miss Hope said she was alone when she received Mr. Smythe's letters. Well, a person can't really be all alone on a street a second before receiving a letter. Or when finishing a letter that's just been received. There must be someone near. He must be mentally invisible."

[102]"Why must there be somebody near?" asked Angus.

[103]"Because," said Father Brown, "unless it was brought by carrier pigeons, somebody must have brought the letter."

[104]"Do you think that Welkin carried his rival's letters to his lady?" asked Flambeau.

[105]"Yes," said the priest. "He had to."

[106]"Oh, I can't stand much more of this!" said Flambeau. "Who is this man? What does he look like? What is the usual costume of a mentally invisible man?"

[107]"He is dressed rather handsomely in blue," said the priest. "And in this costume he entered the Grand Apartments under eight eyes. He killed Smythe in cold blood. And he came down the street carrying the dead body in his arms—"

[108]"Sir," cried Angus, "are you completely mad, or am I?"

[109]"You are not mad," said the priest. "Just a little unobservant. You have not noticed a man such as this, for example."

[110]He took three quick strides forward. And he put his hand on the shoulder of an ordinary postman. He had bustled by them unnoticed.

[111]"Nobody ever notices postmen, somehow," said Father Brown. "Yet they have passions like other men. And they even carry large bags

where a small corpse can be stowed quite easily."

[112]The postman had ducked and tumbled against the garden fence. He was a lean man with a beard. He seemed very ordinary in appearance. But when he turned his face to the men, he had the most severe squint they had ever seen. At once, they knew they had their man.

UNDERSTANDING THE MAIN IDEA

The following questions will demonstrate your understanding of what the story is about, or the *main idea*. Choose the best answer for each question.

1. This story is mainly about

Ⓐ a priest who solves a mystery.

Ⓑ an elegant young lady.

Ⓒ mechanical dummies.

Ⓓ a pastry shop.

2. The story could have been titled

Ⓐ "A Shop in Camden Town."

Ⓑ "Smythe's Silent Service."

Ⓒ "The Grand Apartments."

Ⓓ "The Almost Perfect Crime."

3. Which detail best supports the main idea?

Ⓐ Brightly colored cakes and sweets were displayed in the window of the shop.

Ⓑ Father Brown put his hand on the shoulder of an ordinary postman.

Ⓒ The doorman stood at the bottom of the steps.

Ⓓ In the entryway stood rows of half-human mechanical figures.

4. Find another detail that supports the main idea of this story. Write it on the lines below.

_____

_____

_____

_____

RECALLING FACTS

The following questions will test how well you remember the facts in the story you just read. Choose the best answer for each question.

1. John Angus first saw Laura Hope in

Ⓐ a candy store.

Ⓑ the Red Fish.

Ⓒ a pastry restaurant.

Ⓓ a boardinghouse.

2. The man whom Laura Hope was most concerned about was

Ⓐ Angus.

Ⓑ Isidore Smythe.

Ⓒ Father Brown.

Ⓓ James Welkin.

3. To avoid marrying them, Laura Hope told Isidore Smythe and James Welkin that

Ⓐ they were too ugly.

Ⓑ they must first make their own lives.

Ⓒ she was engaged to someone else.

Ⓓ they frightened her.

4. On the lines below, write the clues Father Brown used to catch the murderer.

_____

_____

_____

_____

_____ ▬ _____

READING BETWEEN THE LINES

An *inference* is a conclusion drawn from facts. A *generalization* is a general statement, idea, or rule that is supported by facts. Analyze the story by choosing the best answer to each question below.

1. **What conclusion can you draw from paragraphs 22–27?**

   Ⓐ Smythe and Welkin knew the real reason Miss Hope wouldn't marry them.

   Ⓑ Smythe and Welkin believed Miss Hope.

   Ⓒ Smythe and Welkin decided to work together to win Miss Hope.

   Ⓓ Smythe's business would soon go broke.

2. **What conclusion can you draw from paragraphs 57–60?**

   Ⓐ Angus was worried about the safety of Smythe.

   Ⓑ Angus was trying to set up Smythe.

   Ⓒ The security guard was really Welkin.

   Ⓓ Angus didn't trust the policeman.

3. **What generalization can you make from this story?**

   Ⓐ All postmen are very plain-looking.

   Ⓑ It's impossible to get away with a crime.

   Ⓒ Sometimes the best place to hide is in plain sight.

   Ⓓ No one who commits a crime in plain sight gets caught.

4. **It can be inferred from the story that**

   Ⓐ Father Brown was a better detective than Flambeau.

   Ⓑ Father Brown's observations were incorrect.

   Ⓒ Father Brown needed Flambeau's help to solve the mystery.

   Ⓓ Father Brown knew all along that Welkin was the murderer.

———————

Crime and Punishment

DETERMINING CAUSE AND EFFECT

Choose the best answers for the following questions to show the relationship between what happened in the story (*effects*) and why those things happened (*causes*).

1. Because he was dressed as a postman, James Welkin was able to do all of the following except

Ⓐ trick Father Brown.

Ⓑ deliver letters to Miss Hope.

Ⓒ enter Smythe's apartment unnoticed.

Ⓓ carry Smythe's body from his house.

2. What happened because Father Brown pointed out that there were footprints going up the steps to Isidore Smythe's building?

Ⓐ The security guard told Father Brown that someone had been there.

Ⓑ Father Brown saw a man enter the apartments.

Ⓒ Smythe was rescued.

Ⓓ Angus thought they were looking for an Invisible Man.

3. Why did James Welkin murder Isidore Smythe?

Ⓐ Smythe had insulted him.

Ⓑ Smythe had visited Miss Hope.

Ⓒ He had been attacked by one of Smythe's mechanical dummies.

Ⓓ He wanted to take over Smythe's business.

4. Why did Father Brown want to know if the policeman had found a light brown sack?

Ⓐ He had lost his somewhere in the area.

Ⓑ He thought Smythe would have dropped it.

Ⓒ He knew the murderer was a postman.

Ⓓ He collected brown sacks.

—————

USING CONTEXT CLUES

Skilled readers can often find the meaning of unfamiliar words by using *context clues*. This means they study the way the words are used in the text. Use the context clues in the excerpts below to determine the meaning of each **bold-faced** word. Then choose the answer that best matches the meaning of the word.

1. " 'I want, please,' " he said with **precision**, 'one cinnamon bun and a small cup of black coffee.' "

CLUE: "It was obvious that he had ordered there before."

Ⓐ question
Ⓑ concern
Ⓒ disgust
Ⓓ accuracy

2. "Between the two rows of the **domestic** dummies lay something more interesting."

CLUE: " 'It's a clockwork invention for doing all the housework by machinery.' "

Ⓐ wax
Ⓑ business
Ⓒ household
Ⓓ professional

3. "He **explored** every corner and cupboard of the apartment in five minutes."

CLUE: "But Isidore Smythe was not in the place, either dead or alive."

Ⓐ searched
Ⓑ inquired
Ⓒ questioned
Ⓓ described

4. "[The doorman] swore that he had not let a **trespasser** by."

CLUE: "[The doorman] was to keep any sort of stranger from coming up the stairs."

Ⓐ detective
Ⓑ intruder
Ⓒ bird
Ⓓ breeze

End-of-Unit Activities

1. **Compare Sherlock Holmes in "The Redheaded League"
   and Father Brown in "The Invisible Man." Fill in the
   Venn diagram below to identify how they are alike and
   different. Find at least three likenesses and six differences.
   Stretch your thinking and avoid such answers as "They are
   both men."**

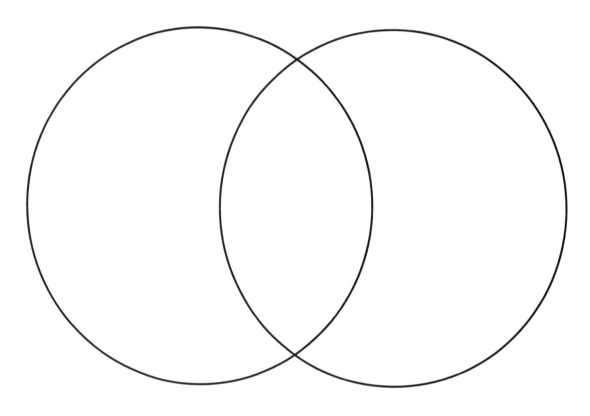

Sherlock Holmes   Father Brown

Crime and Punishment

End-of-Unit Activities

2. **Rank each of the stories in this unit, from the one you liked the most to the one you liked the least. For each story, write one interesting fact you learned. Then tell why you liked the story you ranked *1* the best.**

LESSON 1 Ranking _____

_____

_____

_____

_____

LESSON 2 Ranking _____

_____

_____

_____

_____

LESSON 3 Ranking _____

_____

_____

_____

_____

LESSON 4 Ranking _____

_____

_____

_____

_____

Why did you like the story you ranked *1* the best?

_____

_____

_____

_____

Words-Per-Minute Chart

Directions:

Use the chart to find your words-per-minute reading speed. Refer to the reading time you recorded at the end of each article. Find your reading time in seconds along the left-hand side of the chart or minutes and seconds along the right-hand side of the chart. Your words-per-minute score will be listed next to the time in the column below the appropriate lesson number.

No. of Words	Lesson 1 2315	Lesson 2 1514	Lesson 3 1964	Lesson 4 2870	Minutes and Seconds
80	1736	1136	1473	2153	1:20
100	1389	908	1178	1722	1:40
120	1158	757	982	1435	2:00
140	992	649	842	1230	2:20
160	868	568	737	1076	2:40
180	772	505	655	957	3:00
200	695	454	589	861	3:20
220	631	413	536	783	3:40
240	579	379	491	718	4:00
260	534	349	453	662	4:20
280	496	324	421	615	4:40
300	463	303	393	574	5:00
320	434	284	368	538	5:20
340	409	267	347	506	5:40
360	386	252	327	478	6:00
380	366	239	310	453	6:20
400	347	227	295	431	6:40
420	331	216	281	410	7:00
440	316	206	268	391	7:20
460	302	197	256	374	7:40
480	289	189	246	359	8:00
500	278	182	236	344	8:20
520	267	175	227	331	8:40
540	257	168	218	319	9:00
560	248	162	210	308	9:20
580	239	157	203	297	9:40
600	232	151	196	287	10:00
620	224	147	190	278	10:20
640	217	142	184	269	10:40
660	210	138	179	261	11:00
680	204	134	173	253	11:20
700	198	130	168	246	11:40
720	193	126	164	239	12:00
740	188	123	159	233	12:20
760	183	120	155	227	12:40
780	178	116	151	221	13:00
800	174	114	147	215	13:20
820	169	111	144	210	13:40
840	165	108	140	205	14:00

Seconds

UNIT TWO—

society on trial

The Scopes "Monkey" Trial

by L. L. Owens

Charles Darwin

In 1925, a great tug-of-war was taking place in America. The struggle was between people with scientific views and people with more traditional views.

[2]These viewpoints were often the direct opposites of each other. Debates were heated.

[3]An issue often debated was the belief in divine creation versus the theory of evolution. Both sides had knowledgeable and devoted supporters.

[4]Creationism is the belief in divine creation by God. It is a common religious belief about how the world—and everything in it—came to be. The biblical book of Genesis describes life's beginnings. According to Genesis, God created the world as we know it. He did so in seven days.

[5]Charles Darwin was a naturalist. He and fellow scientist Alfred Russell Wallace proposed the theory of evolution. Their work was influenced by other theorists of the day. Darwin's name, however, is more closely connected with evolution than any other.

[6]Darwin's 1859 book, *The Origin of Species*, explored evolution fully. The theory is often described as "the survival of the fittest." Darwin said that, on average, nature's population is constant. Parents (of all species) tend to produce more offspring than is needed to replace them.

[7]For example, a female bird and her mate produce seven chicks. When the parents die, seven chicks remain. This causes a population growth of five birds.

[8]The increase in offspring results in competition. Then members of a species need to compete for survival. Those who survive have

the strongest, or dominant, traits. And those traits are passed from generation to generation.

[9]This competitive selection of traits can cause species to change, or evolve, with time. And with enough time, a species can change into what should be classified as a new species.

[10]Evolution suggested that the human species may have developed from the same ancestral species as modern apes.

[11]Many people held strong opinions about divine creation. They felt that it should be taught in schools. Others felt that Charles Darwin's theory of evolution should be taught instead.

[12]In February 1925, the Butler Act became law in Tennessee. This act made it unlawful for a teacher in a state-funded school "to teach any theory that denies the story of the divine creation of man as taught in the Bible, and to teach instead that man has descended from a lower order of animals."

[13]This meant that teaching evolution was against the law in Tennessee.

[14]At the time, John T. Scopes was a 24-year-old teacher in Dayton, Tennessee. He believed in Darwin's

theory. So he decided to challenge the law.

[15]The American Civil Liberties Union (ACLU) promised to defend Scopes. So on April 24, Scopes taught his high school science students a lesson. The topic was evolution.

[16]Scopes was arrested two weeks later.

[17]The case was big. The stakes were high. People on both sides wanted the issue decided—once and for all.

[18]The press swarmed to Dayton. A great number of reporters covered the trial. Back then, journalists filed their stories over the telegraph. Dayton had to string new lines.

[19]Pretrial news reports called the trial the "monkey" case. Eager vendors flocked to the scene. They sold every type of monkey souvenir imaginable.

[20]Well-known attorney Clarence Darrow led the ACLU defense team. The other defense attorneys were Arthur Garfield Hays and Dudley Field Malone.

[21]Popular legal and political figure William Jennings Bryan served as chief prosecutor with A. T. Stewart.

[22]Bryan said that the case would be "a duel to the death." He said, "If

evolution wins in Dayton, Christianity goes."

[23] Two legal giants were set to square off in court.

[24] Clarence Darrow represented the defense. He was one of the 20th century's brightest lawyers. He was also one of the most famous.

[25] William Jennings Bryan represented the prosecution. He was a politician and a lawyer. He served as a Democratic Congressman in the 1890s. He ran for president three times and won the Democratic nomination twice. He strongly opposed the teaching of evolution in school. He was called "The Great Commoner." He wanted to preserve traditional thought and customs. His views made the Scopes trial all the more important to him.

[26] The trial began on Friday, July 10, 1925. Nearly 1,000 interested citizens crowded the courtroom.

[27] Darrow argued that the Butler Act violated the U.S. Constitution. He said it took away people's First Amendment and Fourteenth Amendment rights. Those rights included freedom of religion and the right to due process of law.

[28] Stewart gave the prosecution's opening statement. He said that Scopes had violated the Butler Act.

He had also denied the story of creation presented in the Bible.

[29] Defense attorney Malone responded. He said that the prosecution would have to address the two important parts of the Butler Act. It would need to prove that Scopes had denied the validity of creationism and taught that man had descended from a lower order of mammals.

[30] A string of witnesses testified at trial. Scopes' students said they'd been taught that humans evolved from one-cell organisms. The drugstore owner from whom Scopes had bought his textbook testified. He said that the textbook had been approved for sale by the state. A Johns Hopkins University doctor explained the scientific meaning of evolutionary theory. In a surprising move, Darrow called Bryan to the stand. Darrow wanted to question him as an expert on the Bible. Bryan accepted. Through clever questioning, Darrow got Bryan to contradict himself—and the Bible— under oath. Bryan was humiliated.

[31] At the end of the trial, Darrow asked the jury to return a guilty verdict. This was another surprise.

[32] Darrow knew what he was doing, though. He knew that the case could be appealed to the

Tennessee Supreme Court. The judge allowed Darrow's request. So there was no need for the prosecution to continue.

[33]As a result, Bryan was denied his chance to deliver his closing speech. Darrow took pleasure in depriving his rival of the spotlight.

[34]The jury returned a guilty verdict within minutes.

[35]After the verdict, Judge John T. Raulston sentenced Scopes. He ordered Scopes to pay a fine of $100. When asked if he had anything to say, Scopes replied, "Your honor, I feel that I have been convicted of violating an unjust statute. I will continue in the future, as I have in the past, to oppose this law in any way I can. Any other action would be in violation of my ideal of academic freedom—that is, to teach the truth as guaranteed in our Constitution of personal and religious freedom. I think the fine is unjust."

[36]One evening shortly after the trial ended, William Jennings Bryan finished his dinner. He didn't feel well. So he decided to take a nap.

[37]Bryan died in his sleep.

[38]Reporters tracked down Clarence Darrow. He was hiking in the Smoky Mountains.

John Scopes felt he was unjustly convicted.

[39]A reporter said that perhaps Bryan had died of a broken heart.

[40]Darrow replied, "Broken heart nothing. He died of a busted belly." He quickly added, for the rest of the group, "His death is a great loss to the American people."

[41]The Tennessee Supreme Court reversed the Scopes decision one year later. The reversal was based on a technicality.

[42]The judge in the Scopes case

had set the fine. According to the Supreme Court, the jury should have done it instead.

[43] The Supreme Court decided against sending the case back to the lower court. The court said, "Nothing is to be gained by prolonging the life of this bizarre case."

[44] In the end, the Scopes case was largely considered a victory for evolutionists. It had exposed the issue to the nation and made the public think about this theory.

[45] A similar case appeared before the Supreme Court in 1968—43 years after the Scopes trial. The Supreme Court ruled that an Arkansas law, which was much like the Butler Act, was unconstitutional.

[46] The law, said the court, violated the First Amendment requirement of separation between church and state.

[47] The Scopes "monkey" case is history. But the debate over its central issue continues.

If you have been timing your reading speed for this story, record your time below.

_____ : _____

Minutes   **Seconds**

UNDERSTANDING THE MAIN IDEA

The following questions will demonstrate your understanding of what the story is about, or the *main idea*. Choose the best answer for each question.

1. This story is mainly about

Ⓐ the book of Genesis.

Ⓑ the death of William Bryan.

Ⓒ the teaching of evolution vs. creationism.

Ⓓ a monkey that was put on trial.

2. The story could have been titled

Ⓐ "Opposite Viewpoints."

Ⓑ "Divine Creation."

Ⓒ "The Great Commoner."

Ⓓ "The Supreme Court."

3. Which detail best supports the main idea of this story?

Ⓐ John T. Scopes was a 24-year-old teacher in Dayton, Tennessee.

Ⓑ Teaching evolution was against the law in Tennessee.

Ⓒ According to evolution, the increase in offspring results in competition.

Ⓓ Clarence Darrow took pleasure in depriving his rival of the spotlight.

4. Find another detail that supports the main idea of this story. Write it on the lines below.

_____

_____

_____

_____

RECALLING FACTS

The following questions will test how well you remember the facts in the story you just read. Choose the best answer for each question.

1. John Scopes was arrested for teaching

Ⓐ evolution in his science class.

Ⓑ creationism in his science class.

Ⓒ evolution in his religion class.

Ⓓ without a valid license.

2. William Jennings Bryan was called "The Great Commoner" because he

Ⓐ wanted all common people to be able to act freely.

Ⓑ wanted to preserve traditional thought and customs.

Ⓒ was a Communist.

Ⓓ was just a common, relatively unknown lawyer.

3. The theory that describes how only the strong survive is known as

Ⓐ naturalism.

Ⓑ creationism.

Ⓒ traditionalism.

Ⓓ evolution.

4. Judge John T. Ralston ordered John Scopes to

Ⓐ end his teaching career.

Ⓑ spend some time in jail.

Ⓒ pay a fine of $100.

Ⓓ leave the state.

READING BETWEEN THE LINES

An *inference* is a conclusion drawn from facts. A *generalization* is a general statement, idea, or rule that is supported by facts. Analyze the story by choosing the best answer to each question below.

1. **What conclusion can you draw from paragraph 25?**

   Ⓐ Bryan was a naturalist.

   Ⓑ Bryan would have made a good president.

   Ⓒ Bryan believed in divine creation.

   Ⓓ Bryan was poor.

2. **What conclusion can you draw from paragraph 35?**

   Ⓐ Scopes was very firm in his beliefs.

   Ⓑ Scopes believed that his penalty was just.

   Ⓒ Scopes gave up without a fight.

   Ⓓ Scopes agreed to uphold the law.

3. **What generalization can you make from this story?**

   Ⓐ Standing up for one's beliefs at the expense of the law is never a smart idea.

   Ⓑ Sometimes national exposure for an issue is worth as much as a win in court.

   Ⓒ Everyone who challenges the law ends up in jail.

   Ⓓ No laws are final.

4. **It can be inferred from the story that the Scopes trial was called the "monkey" case because**

   Ⓐ Scopes resembled a monkey.

   Ⓑ it dealt with evolution.

   Ⓒ the lawyers were out of control during the trial.

   Ⓓ Scopes had brought a monkey to school.

DETERMINING CAUSE AND EFFECT

Choose the best answers for the following questions to show the relationship between what happened in the story (*effects*) and why those things happened (*causes*).

1. **Because of the Butler Act,**

   Ⓐ teaching divine creation was against the law in Tennessee.

   Ⓑ all teachers were forced to teach evolution.

   Ⓒ teaching evolution was against the law in Tennessee.

   Ⓓ the ACLU promised to prosecute John T. Scopes.

2. **What happened because Clarence Darrow asked the jury to return a guilty verdict?**

   Ⓐ Bryan was denied his chance to deliver his closing speech.

   Ⓑ Bryan delivered a powerful closing speech.

   Ⓒ The jury found Scopes not guilty.

   Ⓓ The jury could not make a decision.

3. **Why did Clarence Darrow say that the Butler Act violated the U.S. Constitution?**

   Ⓐ It took away freedom to vote and freedom of the press.

   Ⓑ It took away freedom of religion and the right to due process.

   Ⓒ It took away the right to do whatever one wants in his or her own classroom.

   Ⓓ It took away equal rights for male and female teachers.

4. **In 1968, why did the Supreme Court rule that an Arkansas law much like the Butler Act was unconstitutional? Write your answer on the lines below.**

   _____

   _____

   _____

   _____

   _____

USING CONTEXT CLUES

Skilled readers can often find the meaning of unfamiliar words by using *context clues*. This means they study the way the words are used in the text. Use the context clues in the excerpts below to determine the meaning of each **bold-faced** word. Then choose the answer that best matches the meaning of the word.

1. "He strongly **opposed** the teaching of evolution in school."

CLUE: "He wanted to preserve traditional thought and customs."

 Ⓐ matched

 Ⓑ disrupted

 Ⓒ was against

 Ⓓ demanded

2. "[The prosecution] would need to prove that Scopes had denied the **validity** of creationism and taught that man had descended from a lower order of mammals."

CLUE: "[Scopes] had also denied the story of creation presented in the Bible."

 Ⓐ strength

 Ⓑ provableness

 Ⓒ effectiveness

 Ⓓ popularity

3. "Darrow took pleasure in **depriving** his rival of the spotlight."

CLUE: "As a result, Bryan was denied his chance to deliver his closing speech."

 Ⓐ disallowing

 Ⓑ restoring

 Ⓒ ignoring

 Ⓓ permitting

4. "The court said, 'Nothing is to be gained by **prolonging** the life of this bizarre case.' "

CLUE: "The Supreme Court decided against sending the case back to a lower court."

 Ⓐ spreading

 Ⓑ proposing

 Ⓒ ending

 Ⓓ continuing

Alger Hiss

Soviet Spy or American Scapegoat?

by L. L. Owens

Alger Hiss

Alger Hiss was born in 1904. He graduated from Johns Hopkins University and Harvard Law School. Then he got a job as a law clerk to Supreme Court Justice Oliver Wendell Holmes.

[2]From there, Hiss went on to a successful government career. He worked for President Franklin D. Roosevelt. Then he worked in the departments of agriculture, justice, and state.

[3]Hiss served as Roosevelt's advisor at the 1945 Yalta Conference. He was also a temporary secretary-general of the United Nations.

[4]In 1946, he was elected president of the Carnegie Endowment for International Peace.

[5]Hiss had built a remarkable career. He'd become a powerful member of the U.S. government.

[6]But all that changed in 1948.

That's when a Soviet spy accused Hiss of espionage. The spy's name was Whittaker Chambers. The resulting scandal would become part of U.S. history.

[7]Whittaker Chambers was born in Philadelphia just after the turn of the 20th century. His given name was Jay Vivian Chambers.

[8]In the 1920s, he changed his first name to Whittaker. That was his mother's maiden name. Chambers would use many different aliases throughout his adult life.

[9]Chambers worked as a journalist. He was an editor at several publications. They included *The New Masses*, *The Daily Worker*, and *Time*.

[10]Chambers joined the Communist Party in 1923. He remained a member until 1938. In 1948, Chambers confessed to having

Richard Nixon served on the Committee on Un-American Activities.

been a Soviet agent. He said that he'd worked for Russia during the 1930s.

[11] He identified Hiss as a member of the same spy ring. He told the House Committee on Un-American Activities that Hiss knowingly passed secret information to the Soviets.

[12] The Committee on Un-American Activities was formed in the U.S. House of Representatives. It began in 1938. Its purpose was to investigate federal employees. It focused on employees' loyalty to the U.S. government and its causes. The committee was mostly interested in identifying Communists.

[13] Congressman and future president Richard M. Nixon served on the committee. He was dedicated to uncovering anti-American plots.

[14] Chambers claimed that Hiss had given him classified information. He claimed that Hiss had taken the papers from the State Department.

[15] As proof, Chambers handed over some papers. He claimed that they had been typed on Hiss's typewriter.

[16] Chambers claimed to have further evidence against Hiss. He produced what would come to be known as "The Pumpkin Papers." They were microfilms of government papers.

[17] According to Chambers, he'd received them from Hiss. And he'd kept them hidden in a pumpkin on his farm.

[18] The House committee held closed-door hearings. They listened to Chambers' testimony. Then they allowed Hiss to testify.

[19] Hiss flatly denied all charges. He called them "complete fabrication." And he said that he did not commit espionage.

[20]He also denied even knowing anyone named Whittaker Chambers.

[21]Congressman Nixon, however, presented Chambers to Hiss. Hiss finally said that he knew Chambers.

[22]But he claimed that he knew Chambers by a different name. Hiss knew Chambers by the name George Crosley.

[23]Meanwhile, Chambers told his story to the media. Hiss then sued Chambers for slander.

[24]Hiss was indicted by a New York federal grand jury. The grand jury charged him with two counts of perjury. They said Hiss had lied under oath. Allegedly, his lies included denials of giving secret government papers to Chambers and speaking to Chambers after January 1, 1937.

[25]The trial began May 31, 1949. Chambers' less-than-perfect record was exposed. His credibility was put to the test. The defense proved that in the past Chambers had been a member of the Communist Party. They also proved that he had stolen books from libraries and been kicked out of Columbia University. They proved he had used seven or more aliases and had committed perjury—twice.

[26]Hiss's attorneys used many character witnesses. They had all known Hiss through various government situations. All swore that Hiss's honesty and his loyalty to the U.S. were too strong to be questioned.

[27]The prosecutors held firm. They presented the papers and the typewriter as the most important pieces of the puzzle.

[28]They felt that they had proven Chambers had papers he could only have received from Hiss. And many of the papers were typed on Hiss's typewriter.

[29]The defense asked a typewriter engineer to study typed material from the typewriter in question. The engineer then built a new typewriter that produced identical type.

[30]A document expert claimed that no expert could tell the difference between papers typed on the two typewriters. This showed that the papers could have come from a typewriter other than Alger Hiss's.

[31]At the end of the trial, the jury was unable to reach a decision. In other words, they were deadlocked.

[32]A second trial began November 17, 1949.

[33]Expert testimony called Chambers' sanity into question. Psychiatrist Dr. Carl Binger said that

Chambers suffered from a psychopathic personality. The symptoms included antisocial behavior, chronic lying, and "the tendency to make false accusations."

[34]Nevertheless, Hiss was found guilty on both counts of perjury. The jury believed that he had lied about his involvement with Chambers.

[35]Hiss eventually served three years and eight months of a five-year sentence. He served his time at the federal prison in Danbury, Connecticut.

[36]Hiss left prison in 1954. Over the next 40 years, he tried to clear his name.

[37]In 1992, the chairman of Russia's military records spoke out. He supported Hiss. He said that a vast search of Soviet records had been done. It had turned up no evidence that Hiss had ever been involved in a spy ring. In fact, the chairman called accusations against Hiss "groundless."

[38]Some scholars said, however, that no search would unearth Soviet intelligence files. So Hiss's guilt or innocence could not be proven by the findings of the search.

[39]In 1996, Soviet cables intercepted by the U.S. during World War II were released. They pointed again to Hiss's guilt. Hiss died that year.

[40]The case is still debated today. Some people think that Hiss was a traitor. They believe that he deserved his perjury conviction. Some even think that Hiss should have been charged with espionage.

[41]Others say that Hiss was framed. Why? Hiss's case broke at a time of great unease in America. Many people feared Soviet Russia and Communist influence in the U.S.

[42]Some say that the Committee on Un-American Activities—or someone else in the government—singled Hiss out. They say that Hiss was used as an example to reassure the public that the government was "catching" Communists and to prove there was a real Communist threat.

If you have been timing your reading speed for this story, record your time below.

_____ : _____

Minutes   ***Seconds***

UNDERSTANDING THE MAIN IDEA

The following questions will demonstrate your understanding of what the story is about, or the *main idea*. Choose the best answer for each question.

1. This story is mainly about

Ⓐ a man accused of spying and perjury.

Ⓑ Congressman Richard M. Nixon.

Ⓒ the Committee on Un-American Activities.

Ⓓ the Communist Party.

2. The story could have been titled

Ⓐ "Soviet Russia."

Ⓑ "An Accused Spy."

Ⓒ "From Congressman to President."

Ⓓ "A Remarkable Career."

3. Which detail best supports the main idea of the story?

Ⓐ Alger Hiss graduated from John Hopkins University and Harvard Law School.

Ⓑ Whittaker Chambers claimed that Hiss had given him classified information.

Ⓒ Nixon would go on to become president.

Ⓓ Chambers had worked as a journalist.

4. Find another detail that supports the main idea of this story. Write it on the lines below.

_____

_____

_____

RECALLING FACTS

The following questions will test how well you remember the facts in the story you just read. Choose the best answer for each question.

1. Whittaker Chambers told the Committee on Un-American Activities that Alger Hiss

Ⓐ passed secret information from the State Department to the Soviets.

Ⓑ passed secret information from the Soviets to the State Department.

Ⓒ served as President Roosevelt's advisor at the 1945 Yalta Conference.

Ⓓ had stolen books from libraries and been kicked out of Columbia University.

2. Whittaker Chambers claimed that the secret papers he handed over had

Ⓐ been written in Hiss's handwriting.

Ⓑ Hiss's personal seal embossed on them.

Ⓒ been typed on Hiss's typewriter.

Ⓓ Hiss's fingerprints on them.

3. The defense proved that Whittaker Chambers had

Ⓐ committed murder.

Ⓑ committed perjury twice.

Ⓒ stolen secret documents.

Ⓓ illegally grown pumpkins.

4. Alger Hiss was

Ⓐ found innocent of perjury.

Ⓑ found guilty on two counts of espionage.

Ⓒ set free without serving a sentence.

Ⓓ found guilty on two counts of perjury.

READING BETWEEN THE LINES

An *inference* is a conclusion drawn from facts. A *generalization* is a general statement, idea, or rule that is supported by facts. Analyze the story by choosing the best answer to each question below.

1. **What conclusion can you draw from paragraph 12?**

   Ⓐ The United States government respected Communists.

   Ⓑ Federal employees were all suspected of being Communists.

   Ⓒ The United States government felt threatened by Communism.

   Ⓓ Loyalty was not valued by the United States government.

2. **What conclusion can you draw from paragraphs 32–34?**

   Ⓐ The jury was convinced that Chambers was not sane.

   Ⓑ The psychiatrist's testimony didn't matter to the jury.

   Ⓒ The psychiatrist was lying under oath.

   Ⓓ The jury sympathized with Alger Hiss.

3. **What generalization can you make from this story?**

   Ⓐ Trials always reveal the truth about a case in the end.

   Ⓑ All Americans believe the verdicts that judges or juries declare.

   Ⓒ Some cases remain a mystery long after the trials are over.

   Ⓓ Defendants never admit their guilt, no matter what the verdict.

4. **It can be inferred from the story that**

   Ⓐ this case will continue to be debated.

   Ⓑ the jury returned the wrong verdict.

   Ⓒ there was no need for a second trial.

   Ⓓ Hiss was innocent.

DETERMINING CAUSE AND EFFECT

Choose the best answers for the following questions to show the relationship between what happened in the story (*effects*) and why those things happened (*causes*).

1. **Because Whittaker Chambers told his story to the media,**

    ⒜ Hiss demanded equal media time.

    ⒝ Hiss was cleared of all charges.

    ⒞ Hiss sued him for slander.

    ⒟ Hiss was found guilty of perjury.

2. **What happened because the jury was unable to reach a decision in Alger Hiss's trial?**

    ⒜ Hiss was set free indefinitely.

    ⒝ Chambers was arrested for perjury.

    ⒞ Hiss's innocence was proven.

    ⒟ A second trial was held.

3. **Why were the microfilms of government papers known as the "pumpkin papers"?**

    ⒜ Hiss had printed them on pumpkin-colored paper.

    ⒝ The papers were delivered on Halloween.

    ⒞ Chambers had hidden the papers in a pumpkin on his farm.

    ⒟ The papers referred to a secret experiment on pumpkins.

4. **Why do some people think Alger Hiss was framed? Write your answer on the lines below.**

    _____

    _____

    _____

    _____

USING CONTEXT CLUES

Skilled readers can often find the meaning of unfamiliar words by using *context clues*. This means they study the way the words are used in the text. Use the context clues in the excerpts below to determine the meaning of each **bold-faced** word. Then choose the answer that best matches the meaning of the word.

1. "Chambers would use many different **aliases** throughout his adult life."

CLUE: "In the 1920s, he changed his name to Whittaker. That was his mother's maiden name."

    Ⓐ businesses

    Ⓑ families

    Ⓒ spies

    Ⓓ identities

2. "Hiss was **indicted** by a New York federal grand jury."

CLUE: "The jury charged him with two counts of perjury."

    Ⓐ freed

    Ⓑ accused

    Ⓒ hired

    Ⓓ criticized

3. "[Chambers'] **credibility** was put to the test."

CLUE: "[The defense] also proved that he had stolen books from libraries and been kicked out of Columbia University. They proved he had used seven or more aliases and had committed perjury—twice."

    Ⓐ intelligence

    Ⓑ ability

    Ⓒ honesty

    Ⓓ patience

4. "In fact, the chairman called accusations against Hiss '**groundless**.' "

CLUE: "It had turned up no evidence that Hiss had ever been involved in a spy ring."

    Ⓐ without support

    Ⓑ skyward

    Ⓒ brilliant

    Ⓓ true

A Step Forward

Brown v. Board of Education

by L. L. Owens

Linda Smith, the former Linda Brown, stood in front of her school in Topeka, Kansas.

In September 1950, Linda Brown was about to start third grade. She lived with her family in Topeka, Kansas.

[2] Schools in Topeka were segregated. Linda, a black child, was not allowed to attend the school for white children.

[3] To get to school, Linda had to leave home early in the morning. She had to walk alone through a busy switchyard. Then she had to wait for a bus. The school was about one mile from home.

[4] The all-white school was nearer the Browns' home. It was a safer seven-block walk. So Oliver Brown decided to enroll Linda there. Oliver was Linda's dad.

[5] After all, Brown reasoned, it would be much easier for Linda to get to school—safer too. And why should young Linda have to go to all that trouble? The fact that she was black—that her skin simply was "not white"—seemed a ridiculous reason.

[6] The school principal promptly turned away the Browns. He would not allow Linda to enroll.

[7] Brown went to see McKinley Burnett. Burnett was head of Topeka's branch of the National Association for the Advancement of Colored People (NAACP).

[8] The NAACP decided to help Brown file a lawsuit. It was time to fight for an end to segregation in public schools.

[9] The claim was that school segregation violated African American students' 14th Amendment rights. That meant that African American students weren't being allowed equal protection under the

law. The court case was referred to as *Brown v. the Board of Education of Topeka, Kansas.*

[10]During that era, segregation was common in Kansas and other Southern states as well. And it was not just in schools. Segregated bathrooms, hotels, theaters, and restaurants were standard.

[11]The lawsuit, however, would address only the public schools. The lawyers argued that black children were being unfairly denied educational opportunities that white children received.

Separate drink fountains were common in the 1950s in segregated states like Kansas.

[12]The lawyers also said that simply improving all-black schools was a poor solution. Black children would still suffer by being educated separately from their white peers.

[13]The U.S. District Court of Kansas ruled. They decided that segregation would continue.

[14]The case was appealed. It went straight to the U.S. Supreme Court. That court heard it twice.

[15]The decision was announced on May 17, 1954. Chief Justice Earl Warren said, "We conclude that in the field of public education, the doctrine of 'separate but equal' has no place. Separate educational facilities are inherently unequal."

[16]This ended legal segregation in public schools.

[17]Warren wrote the court's opinion. It explained how the court reached its decision.

[18]In this case, all nine justices agreed. Part of the opinion read, "In approaching this problem, we cannot turn the clock back to 1868 when the 14th Amendment was adopted. . . . We must consider public education in light of its full development and its present place in American life."

[19]The court had concluded that "segregation deprived members of

76

the minority race of equal opportunities."

[20]They said that segregation "generates a feeling of inferiority . . . that may affect . . . hearts and minds in a way unlikely to be undone."

[21]In other words, children denied equal educational opportunities might have a more difficult time as adults. They might lack the motivation—or even the knowledge—to succeed. And this was clearly unfair.

[22]Although the Supreme Court had ruled, change was slow.

[23]In 1955, the court said that all American schools should end segregation. And that they should do so "with all deliberate speed."

[24]During the civil rights movement of the 1960s, all forms of segregation were banned. But it still took 20 years of "deliberate speed" to desegregate the nation's schools.

[25]Oliver Brown didn't live to see that. But he would have been proud because he helped make it happen.

If you have been timing your reading speed for this story, record your time below.

_____ : _____

Minutes   **Seconds**

UNDERSTANDING THE MAIN IDEA

The following questions will demonstrate your understanding of what the story is about, or the *main idea*. Choose the best answer for each question.

1. This story is mainly about

Ⓐ students in an all-white school.

Ⓑ desegregating public schools.

Ⓒ the NAACP.

Ⓓ a school principal.

2. The story could have been titled

Ⓐ "A Victory for Civil Rights."

Ⓑ "The History of Education."

Ⓒ "The Supreme Court."

Ⓓ "Chief Justice Earl Warren—A Great American."

3. Which detail best supports the main idea of this story?

Ⓐ In September 1950, Linda Brown was about to start third grade.

Ⓑ Brown's lawyers argued that black children were being unfairly denied educational opportunities that white children received.

Ⓒ McKinley Burnett was head of Topeka's branch of the NAACP.

Ⓓ During the civil rights movement, all forms of segregation were banned.

4. Find another detail that supports the main idea of this story. Write it on the lines below.

_____

_____

_____

RECALLING FACTS

The following questions will test how well you remember the facts in the story you just read. Choose the best answer for each question.

1. The lawsuit filed by Oliver Brown addressed

Ⓐ all schools.

Ⓑ only private schools.

Ⓒ only public schools.

Ⓓ only Topeka schools.

2. The decision that segregation would continue was made by

Ⓐ Chief Justice Earl Warren.

Ⓑ the Supreme Court.

Ⓒ the Board of Education.

Ⓓ the U.S. District Court of Kansas.

3. Chief Justice Earl Warren believed that

Ⓐ separate educational facilities were acceptable.

Ⓑ segregation was just a part of life.

Ⓒ separate educational facilities were unequal.

Ⓓ segregation was not a violation of the 14th Amendment.

4. In 1955, the Supreme Court said that

Ⓐ all American schools should be segregated.

Ⓑ the case of *Brown v. the Board of Education* should be reopened.

Ⓒ all American schools should end segregation.

Ⓓ it expected desegregation to take a long time.

Crime and Punishment

READING BETWEEN THE LINES

An *inference* is a conclusion drawn from facts. A *generalization* is a general statement, idea, or rule that is supported by facts. Analyze the story by choosing the best answer to each question below.

1. **What conclusion can you draw from paragraphs 1–7?**

   Ⓐ Oliver Brown was determined and persistent.

   Ⓑ Oliver Brown was a troublemaker.

   Ⓒ The principal of the all-white school wanted to end segregation.

   Ⓓ Linda Brown was lazy and spoiled.

2. **What conclusion can you draw from paragraphs 23–24?**

   Ⓐ The Supreme Court filed lawsuits against all schools that were still segregated after a year.

   Ⓑ All schools willingly desegregated.

   Ⓒ The Supreme Court was trying to hasten desegregation.

   Ⓓ The schools were trying to desegregate as fast as they could.

3. **What generalization can you make from this story?**

   Ⓐ All white people were in favor of segregating schools.

   Ⓑ Some African Americans were in favor of keeping schools segregated.

   Ⓒ Some schools never desegregated.

   Ⓓ Some people believed that segregation was harmful to students.

4. **It can be inferred from the story that**

   Ⓐ the U.S. Supreme Court has more power than the U.S. District Court of Kansas.

   Ⓑ the U.S. Supreme Court was not supposed to listen to Brown's case.

   Ⓒ the U.S. Supreme Court was upset that Brown had not taken his case directly to them.

   Ⓓ the U.S. Supreme Court only hears cases that deal with discrimination due to race.

DETERMINING CAUSE AND EFFECT

Choose the best answers for the following questions to show the relationship between what happened in the story (*effects*) and why those things happened (*causes*).

1. **Because the principal turned the Browns away, Oliver Brown**

   Ⓐ filed a lawsuit.

   Ⓑ went directly to the Supreme Court.

   Ⓒ contacted the court in Kansas.

   Ⓓ enrolled his daughter in another school.

2. **What happened because the case was appealed?**

   Ⓐ The Supreme Court dismissed the case.

   Ⓑ Oliver Brown dropped the lawsuit.

   Ⓒ The Supreme Court heard the case.

   Ⓓ The NAACP refused to represent Brown any longer.

3. **On another sheet of paper, write a note that Oliver Brown may have written to the principal of the all-white school, explaining why Linda should be able to attend.**

4. **Why did the Supreme Court end legal segregation in public schools?**

   Ⓐ The court said that minorities weren't being given equal opportunities.

   Ⓑ The court said that white students felt inferior to minority students.

   Ⓒ The court was afraid that minority students would drop out of public schools and attend private schools.

   Ⓓ The court didn't want children of different races to attend the same schools.

———————

USING CONTEXT CLUES

Skilled readers can often find the meaning of unfamiliar words by using *context clues*. This means they study the way the words are used in the text. Use the context clues in the excerpts below to determine the meaning of each **bold-faced** word. Then choose the answer that best matches the meaning of the word.

1. "After all, Brown **reasoned**, it would be much easier for Linda to get to school—safer too."

CLUE: "To get to school, Linda had to leave home early in the morning. She had to walk alone through a busy switchyard."

   Ⓐ excused

   Ⓑ angered

   Ⓒ walked

   Ⓓ thought

2. "Schools in Topeka were **segregated**."

CLUE: " Linda, a black child, was not allowed to attend the school for white children."

   Ⓐ fair

   Ⓑ disconnected

   Ⓒ selected

   Ⓓ separated

3. "The claim was that school segregation **violated** African American students' 14th Amendment rights."

CLUE: "The lawyers argued that black children were being unfairly denied educational opportunities that white children received."

   Ⓐ upheld

   Ⓑ suffered

   Ⓒ ignored

   Ⓓ discovered

4. "They said that segregation 'generates a feeling of **inferiority** . . . that may affect . . . hearts and minds in a way unlikely to be undone.' "

CLUE: "In other words, children denied equal educational opportunities might have a more difficult time as adults."

   Ⓐ confidence

   Ⓑ pressure

   Ⓒ happiness

   Ⓓ unimportance

The Los Angeles Police Officers' "Rodney King Beating" Trials

Rodney King

by L. L. Owens

On March 3, 1991, the Los Angeles police chased Rodney King for three miles. They finally caught him. They began arrest procedures.

[2]But something went terribly wrong.

[3]Rodney King was a young African American. Four white police officers brutally beat him. At least a dozen officers watched.

[4]The whole thing was caught on videotape. The officers, of course, had no idea at the time that anyone was recording their actions.

[5]Official arrest reports claimed that King refused to get out of his car and that he put up a violent struggle against the officers. The reports explained that the officers had needed to use force to subdue King.

[6]The videotape contradicted the arrest reports, though. The tape showed that King was beaten to the ground.

[7]The officers punched King. They kicked him. They swung metal batons at his head. They even used stun guns. King was unable to fight back.

[8]Faced with the public videotape and the differing police reports, a grand jury looked into the matter. They indicted four of the officers involved. They were Theodore J. Briseno, Stacey C. Koon, Laurence M. Powell, and Timothy E. Wind. The men were charged with assault, using excessive force, and filing a false report.

[9]News of these events sold newspapers and kept Americans glued to the television. It seemed

that the media showed clips from the beating video with every mention of the story.

[10]People everywhere were shocked by the apparent police brutality. Civil rights leaders charged that the incident was racially motivated. Los Angeles citizens were angered by the actions of the officers who were supposed to protect the city.

[11]There was so much media attention that the trial was moved to Simi Valley, California. The location was somewhat removed from Los Angeles. The hope was that the move would ensure a fair trial.

[12]At trial, a California Highway Patrol officer testified against Powell. That officer was Melanie Singer. She said that Powell had used unnecessary force against King.

[13]Other information for the prosecution claimed that Powell and Wind had lost control of their actions. It also claimed that Koon, the highest-ranking officer of the group, did not stop his men. It said the officers filed false reports because they knew that their actions had been illegal.

[14]The defense claimed that the officers believed King was on drugs and dangerous. They also said that Koon and Briseno had tried to end Powell's beating of King and that the officers' actions were the only way to gain control of King.

[15]The jury found the four officers not guilty. It was a surprise verdict.

[16]The acquittal angered the public. Riots broke out in Los Angeles immediately.

[17]Angry mobs terrorized the city for three days straight. They set fires. They smashed windows. They looted businesses. They hurt—and killed—other people.

[18]On the second day, King pleaded with rioters. He asked them to stop.

[19]"It's just not right," he said. "It's not right. I just want to say, can we all get along? Can we get along?"

[20]During the riots 1,100 buildings were either damaged or destroyed. About 2,000 people were injured, and 58 people died. Property damage reached $1 billion.

[21]Reginald Denny was one of the 2,000 people injured.

[22]Denny, a white truck driver, drove into the riot area. He was trying to do his job. But rioters refused to let him safely pass through.

[23]Denny was pulled from his truck. Two African American men

beat and kicked him. They stomped on him. And they smashed his head with a brick. Denny suffered 90 broken bones in his face.

The worst riots in modern U.S. history began after the verdict of the Rodney King trial.

[24]The violence was caused by people who were angered at police brutality. Denny—like King—was powerless to stop it.

[25]News helicopters hovering above the scene captured it all on videotape.

[26]The outcry over the results of the first trial was so great that the issue remained unresolved.

[27]Soon, the government charged Briseno, Koon, Powell, and Wind with violating Rodney King's civil rights.

[28]A second trial began on February 3, 1993.

[29]At the end of the trial, the jury deliberated. Los Angeles—and the world—nervously awaited the verdict. Many feared more rioting if the officers were again found not guilty.

[30]This time, Briseno and Wind were acquitted. Koon and Powell were convicted.

[31]Los Angeles breathed a bit easier. People felt that justice had been better served with this decision.

[32]Another decision would happen in April 1994. That's when a jury awarded King $3.8 million in damages. King had sued the city of

Los Angeles. And he'd won.

[33]King was later asked whether "anything good" had come from his ordeal. He replied, "It has shined the light on police brutality."

[34]Several years after the trials, King commented that police attitudes had improved. He also said, "As far as us as individuals, we have a lot of work to do."

> **If you have been timing your reading speed for this story, record your time below.**
>
> _____ : _____
>
> *Minutes   Seconds*

UNDERSTANDING THE MAIN IDEA

The following questions will demonstrate your understanding of what the story is about, or the *main idea*. Choose the best answer for each question.

1. This story is mainly about

Ⓐ the history of the Los Angeles Police Department.

Ⓑ Los Angeles.

Ⓒ a wild police chase.

Ⓓ the trial of a police brutality case.

2. The story could have been titled

Ⓐ "The Story of the LAPD."

Ⓑ "Important Testimony."

Ⓒ "The Crime Caught on Tape."

Ⓓ "I Love L.A."

3. Which detail best supports the main idea of this story?

Ⓐ Four white police officers brutally beat Rodney King.

Ⓑ Two thousand people were injured in the riots.

Ⓒ Reginald Denny had 90 broken bones in his face.

Ⓓ King sued the city of Los Angeles.

4. Find another detail that supports the main idea. Write it on the lines below.

_____

_____

_____

_____

RECALLING FACTS

The following questions will test how well you remember the facts in the story you just read. Choose the best answer for each question.

1. Rodney King was arrested because he

Ⓐ robbed a bank.

Ⓑ assaulted a police officer.

Ⓒ tried to outrun police officers.

Ⓓ stole a video camera.

2. The jury at the first trial mostly believed what they

Ⓐ saw on the videotape.

Ⓑ heard from the defense.

Ⓒ heard from the prosecution.

Ⓓ read in the newspapers.

3. Rodney King asked rioters to

Ⓐ stop rioting.

Ⓑ continue rioting until the officers were convicted.

Ⓒ attack all white people.

Ⓓ take over the Los Angeles Police Department.

4. At the end of the second trial,

Ⓐ all four officers were convicted.

Ⓑ all four officers were acquitted.

Ⓒ two officers were convicted.

Ⓓ three officers were acquitted.

Crime and Punishment

READING BETWEEN THE LINES

An *inference* is a conclusion drawn from facts. A *generalization* is a general statement, idea, or rule that is supported by facts. Analyze the story by choosing the best answer to each question below.

1. What conclusion can you draw from paragraph 12?

Ⓐ Melanie Singer was a witness for the defense.

Ⓑ Singer witnessed the beating of King.

Ⓒ All California Highway Patrol officers are women.

Ⓓ Other California Highway Patrol officers would testify.

2. What conclusion can you draw from paragraphs 21–23?

Ⓐ Denny was an innocent victim.

Ⓑ Denny didn't enjoy his work.

Ⓒ Denny almost died from his injuries.

Ⓓ Denny deserved his beating.

3. What generalization can you make from this story?

Ⓐ Some police officers try to get away with criminal acts.

Ⓑ All police officers take the law into their own hands.

Ⓒ No police officers are considered dangerous to society.

Ⓓ It is always difficult to convict police officers.

4. It can be inferred from the story that

Ⓐ Officers Powell and Koon were doing their job.

Ⓑ Officers Powell and Koon were in control of their actions.

Ⓒ Many people were concerned about police brutality.

Ⓓ Police brutality doesn't really exist in the U.S.

DETERMINING CAUSE AND EFFECT

Choose the best answers for the following questions to show the relationship between what happened in the story (*effects*) and why those things happened (*causes*).

1. Because the acquittal of the officers angered the public,

Ⓐ the Los Angeles Police Department was shut down.

Ⓑ King was awarded $3.8 million.

Ⓒ Denny tried to do his job.

Ⓓ riots broke out in Los Angeles.

2. What happened because Reginald Denny tried to do his job?

Ⓐ He was pulled from his truck and beaten.

Ⓑ He was fired.

Ⓒ News helicopters with video cameras hovered above him.

Ⓓ He was charged with violating King's civil rights.

3. Why did the grand jury look into the beating of Rodney King?

Ⓐ The civil rights leaders were outraged.

Ⓑ There was so much media attention.

Ⓒ The citizens of Los Angeles were angry.

Ⓓ A videotape contradicted police reports.

4. Why was Rodney King awarded $3.8 million in 1994?

Ⓐ He had sued the city of Los Angeles and won.

Ⓑ He had sued Denny and won.

Ⓒ He had been paid by the officers who beat him.

Ⓓ He was paid by the citizens who rioted.

———■———

USING CONTEXT CLUES

Skilled readers can often find the meaning of unfamiliar words by using *context clues*. This means they study the way the words are used in the text. Use the context clues in the excerpts below to determine the meaning of each **bold-faced** word. Then choose the answer that best matches the meaning of the word.

1. "The videotape **contradicted** the arrest reports, though."

CLUE: "The tape showed that King was beaten to the ground."

  Ⓐ showed

  Ⓑ confirmed

  Ⓒ went against

  Ⓓ studied

2. "The reports explained that the officers had needed to use force to **subdue** King."

CLUE: "Official arrest reports claimed that King refused to get out of his car and that he put up a violent struggle against the officers."

  Ⓐ bother

  Ⓑ overpower

  Ⓒ reduce

  Ⓓ help

3. "The hope was that the move would **ensure** a fair trial."

CLUE: "There was so much media attention that the trial was moved to Simi Valley, California."

  Ⓐ decide

  Ⓑ learn

  Ⓒ decline

  Ⓓ guarantee

4. "Angry mobs **terrorized** the city for three days straight."

CLUE: "They set fires . . . smashed windows . . . looted businesses . . . hurt—and killed—other people."

  Ⓐ terrified

  Ⓑ toured

  Ⓒ avoided

  Ⓓ surprised

End-of-Unit Activities

1. **The title of this unit was "Society on Trial." Choose one of the four cases featured and explain how society was on trial.**

_____

_____

_____

_____

_____

_____

_____

Explain whether you agree or disagree with the outcome.

_____

_____

_____

_____

_____

_____

How has this trial affected life today? Explain.

_____

_____

_____

_____

_____

_____

Crime and Punishment

End-of-Unit Activities

2. **Rank each of the stories in this unit, from the one you liked the most to the one you liked the least. For each story, write one interesting fact you learned. Then tell why you liked the story you ranked _1_ the best.**

LESSON 5 Ranking _____

_____

_____

_____

_____

LESSON 6 Ranking _____

_____

_____

_____

_____

LESSON 7 Ranking _____

_____

_____

_____

_____

LESSON 8 Ranking _____

_____

_____

_____

_____

Why did you like the story you ranked _1_ the best?

_____

_____

_____

Words-Per-Minute Chart
UNIT TWO

Directions:

Use the chart to find your words-per-minute reading speed. Refer to the reading time you recorded at the end of each article. Find your reading time in seconds along the left-hand side of the chart or minutes and seconds along the right-hand side of the chart. Your words-per-minute score will be listed next to the time in the column below the appropriate lesson number.

No. of Words	Lesson 5 1341	Lesson 6 1101	Lesson 7 601	Lesson 8 815	
80	1006	826	451	611	1:20
100	805	661	361	489	1:40
120	671	551	301	408	2:00
140	575	472	258	349	2:20
160	503	413	225	306	2:40
180	447	367	200	272	3:00
200	402	330	180	245	3:20
220	366	300	164	222	3:40
240	335	275	150	204	4:00
260	309	254	139	188	4:20
280	287	236	129	175	4:40
300	268	220	120	163	5:00
320	251	206	113	153	5:20
340	237	194	106	144	5:40
360	224	184	100	136	6:00
380	212	174	95	129	6:20
400	201	165	90	122	6:40
420	192	157	86	116	7:00
440	183	150	82	111	7:20
460	175	144	78	106	7:40
480	168	138	75	102	8:00
500	161	132	72	98	8:20
520	155	127	69	94	8:40
540	149	122	67	91	9:00
560	144	118	64	87	9:20
580	139	114	62	84	9:40
600	134	110	60	82	10:00
620	130	107	58	79	10:20
640	126	103	56	76	10:40
660	122	100	55	74	11:00
680	118	97	53	72	11:20
700	115	94	52	70	11:40
720	112	92	50	68	12:00
740	109	89	49	66	12:20
760	106	87	47	64	12:40
780	103	85	46	63	13:00
800	101	83	45	61	13:20
820	98	81	44	60	13:40
840	96	79	43	58	14:00

Seconds

Minutes and Seconds

Crime and Punishment

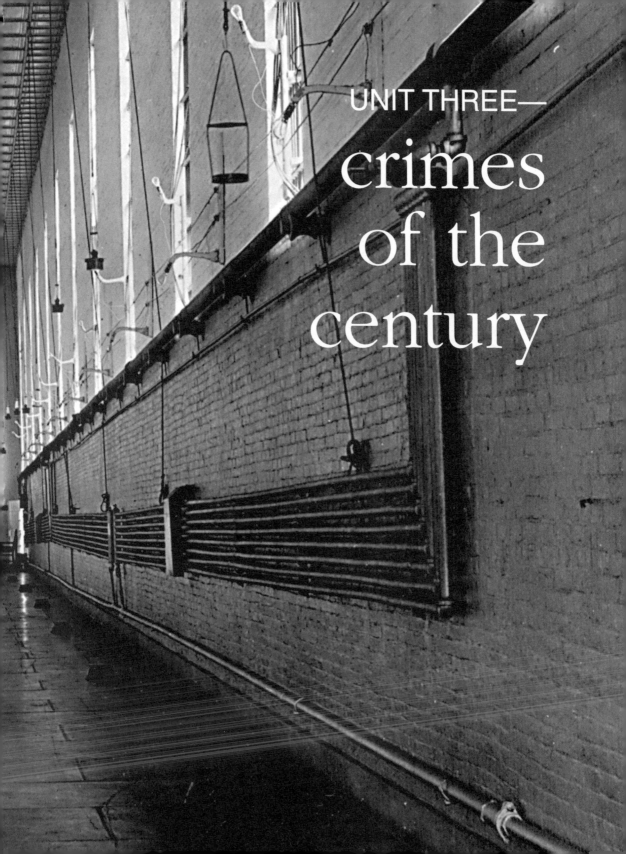

UNIT THREE—

crimes
of the
century

The Lindbergh Baby Kidnapping

by L. L. Owens

Charles and Anne Morrow Lindbergh

[1]On March 1, 1932, Charles and Anne Morrow Lindbergh's baby was kidnapped. He was taken from his crib in the family's Hopewell, New Jersey, home.

[2]The world watched as the couple tried to get him back. The public mourned when he was found dead. And they rejoiced when Bruno Richard Hauptmann was convicted of the murder.

[3]In the early 1930s, there were organized kidnapping rings. They had sprung up in every major U.S. city.

[4]The criminals in these rings stole children. Then they demanded money from suffering parents. That money was called ransom. It was asked for in exchange for the child.

[5]The wealthy were popular targets. And the Lindberghs were wealthy.

[6]This baby's name was Charles A. Lindbergh Jr. He was 20 months old.

[7]Anne put him to bed that night. He had a cold. So she made sure he was warm and comfortable.

[8]Anne left his side at 7:30 p.m.

[9]The nursemaid was Betty Gow. She was still in the nursery when Anne left. She tidied up. She made sure the baby was covered. Then she opened a French window halfway.

[10]Betty checked a short time later. The baby was fast asleep.

[11]The Lindberghs had dinner at about 8:30.

[12]At 10:00, Betty entered the nursery. It was time for another routine check. She shut the window and turned on the heater.

[13]Then she turned toward the crib. It was empty!

[14]She quickly found Anne. She asked, "Do you have the baby, Mrs. Lindbergh?"

[15]Anne did not.

[16]"Perhaps Colonel Lindbergh has him then," said Betty.

[17]The women searched the house. Charles didn't have the baby. None of the other servants had the baby. He was gone.

[18]Charles examined the baby's room. The window was unlatched. It was open just a crack. A white envelope rested on the sill.

[19]Charles didn't touch it. He knew it was a ransom note. And it was evidence.

[20]He called the police at 10:25. Within 20 minutes, state law enforcement agencies had been notified. By 11:00, the investigation was well under way.

[21]The police found four main pieces of evidence. The first was the ransom note. The second was an abandoned homemade ladder. The third was a shoe print in the mud near the ladder, and the fourth was a chisel near the ladder.

[22]A rung on the ladder was broken. Police thought it had likely broken as the kidnapper came back down the ladder. So the kidnapper— with the baby—had probably fallen about five feet to the ground.

[23]The kidnapper clearly knew the layout of the house. And that person knew the schedule of the household. Police felt that more than one person had helped plan the crime.

[24]The handwriting on the note was awkward. Experts thought the writer was probably Scandinavian. Or perhaps the writer was German. They decided this because of the placement of the dollar signs. Also, the spellings used showed that the writer didn't know English that well.

[25]The Lindberghs were heartsick. Anne wrote letters to help her think through the situation. Charles tried to control the investigation. But both were helpless.

[26]The public followed news of the case for the next several weeks. The Lindberghs received many fake ransom notes. Floods of mail from well-wishers also arrived.

[27]Soon a meeting with the kidnapper was set up. A go-between delivered $50,000 to the supposed kidnapper.

[28]In exchange, Charles received instructions. They told him where to find the baby. But the baby wasn't there.

[29]On May 12, the couple's worst nightmare came true. The baby was found dead. He had been left in the woods just a few miles from home.

[30]It appeared that he had died from a blow to the head. Police felt that he had been dead since the night he was taken. He may have even died in the fall from the ladder.

[31]It was two years before an arrest was made.

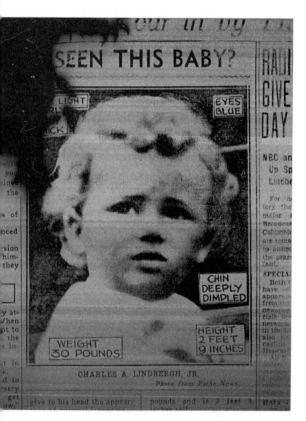

Newspapers advertised to help find the kidnapped baby.

[32]Bruno Richard Hauptmann was a carpenter. And he was a German immigrant. He had entered the country illegally.

[33]In September 1934, Hauptmann bought gas. He paid with a $10 gold certificate. This was an unusual way to pay.

[34]The federal government first issued gold certificates in 1863. The paper currency notes were printed with orange ink. They were backed by 100 percent reserves of gold coin. They could be cashed in on demand. General use ended in 1933.

[35]The gas station attendant noted Hauptmann's license number. And he took the certificate to the bank.

[36]The bill was identified as part of the Lindbergh ransom money. Hauptmann was soon arrested.

[37]Police found more ransom money in his garage. They also found the phone number of the Lindberghs' go-between. It was written on the wall in a closet.

[38]The trial was a major media event. The public watched with great interest. Everyone wanted justice for "Lucky Lindy," his beautiful wife, and their slain child.

[39]Things went badly for Hauptmann. There was much circumstantial evidence against him.

Crime and Punishment

For one thing, he possessed some of the ransom money. Handwriting experts also testified that he had written the ransom notes.

[40] Also, the ladder was traced to him.

[41] No witnesses placed Hauptmann at the scene of the crime. The footprint wasn't proven to be his. And his fingerprints were not found in the baby's room. They were not on the ransom notes either.

[42] Still, he was found guilty. He was electrocuted April 3, 1936. The public felt that justice had been served.

[43] As recently as 1992, Hauptmann's widow tried to clear his name. She believed her husband was framed. And his conviction should be overturned.

[44] Some experts agree with Mrs. Hauptmann. They say that the case was mishandled, and it should be reopened.

[45] So far, the courts have been unwilling to take another look.

[46] One thing seems clear, though. The Lindbergh baby case will be discussed well into the 21st century.

> *If you have been timing your reading speed for this story, record your time below.*
>
> _____ : _____
>
> **Minutes**   **Seconds**

UNDERSTANDING THE MAIN IDEA

The following questions will demonstrate your understanding of what the story is about, or the *main idea*. Choose the best answer for each question.

1. This story is mainly about

Ⓐ a wealthy couple.

Ⓑ a famous kidnapping and ransom.

Ⓒ a sick child.

Ⓓ the life of Charles Lindbergh Sr.

2. The story could have been titled

Ⓐ "Those Lucky Lindberghs."

Ⓑ "A Broken Ladder."

Ⓒ "A Senseless Death for Ransom."

Ⓓ "A Happy Ending."

3. Which detail supports the main idea of this story?

Ⓐ Bruno Hauptmann was found with the Lindbergh ransom money.

Ⓑ Anne Lindbergh wrote letters to help her think through the situation.

Ⓒ Hauptmann was a carpenter.

Ⓓ Charles Lindbergh Jr. had a cold.

4. Find another detail that supports the main idea. Write it on the lines below.

_____

_____

_____

_____

RECALLING FACTS

The following questions will test how well you remember the facts in the story you just read. Choose the best answer for each question.

1. On the windowsill of the baby's room, Charles Lindbergh found

Ⓐ a glove.

Ⓑ a piece of torn clothing.

Ⓒ blood.

Ⓓ an envelope.

2. The piece of evidence that caused police to arrest Bruno Hauptmann was a

Ⓐ ladder.

Ⓑ gold certificate.

Ⓒ chisel.

Ⓓ shoe print.

3. During Bruno Hauptmann's trial, it was not proven that

Ⓐ the gold certificate was part of the Lindbergh ransom money.

Ⓑ the footprint found at the scene was his.

Ⓒ he had the phone number of the Lindbergh's go-between.

Ⓓ the ladder was his.

4. Bruno Hauptmann was found guilty and sentenced to

Ⓐ 30 years in prison.

Ⓑ life in prison.

Ⓒ death by electrocution.

Ⓓ life in a mental hospital.

READING BETWEEN THE LINES

An *inference* is a conclusion drawn from facts. A *generalization* is a general statement, idea, or rule that is supported by facts. Analyze the story by choosing the best answer to each question below.

1. **What conclusion can you draw from paragraphs 27–28?**

   Ⓐ The Lindberghs found it difficult to part with their money.

   Ⓑ The kidnapper could not be trusted.

   Ⓒ The money the go-between delivered wasn't real.

   Ⓓ The Lindberghs had to take out a loan to come up with the money.

2. **What conclusion can you draw from paragraph 38?**

   Ⓐ The public blamed Charles Lindbergh for his baby's death.

   Ⓑ The Lindberghs were not popular with the public.

   Ⓒ The entire public attended the trial.

   Ⓓ The Lindberghs were a popular family.

3. **What generalization can you make from this story?**

   Ⓐ Carpenters never commit crimes.

   Ⓑ All criminals get what they deserve.

   Ⓒ No one commits a crime on his or her own.

   Ⓓ Many criminals give themselves away in the end.

4. **It can be inferred from the story that**

   Ⓐ Mrs. Hauptmann helped her husband commit the crime.

   Ⓑ Mrs. Hauptmann was devoted to her husband.

   Ⓒ Hauptmann was definitely framed.

   Ⓓ Hauptmann's case was mishandled.

DETERMINING CAUSE AND EFFECT

Choose the best answers for the following questions to show the relationship between what happened in the story (*effects*) and why those things happened (*causes*).

1. **Because the handwriting on the ransom note was awkward, experts thought the writer**

   Ⓐ was probably European.

   Ⓑ was probably a child.

   Ⓒ was writing with his or her left hand.

   Ⓓ had a hand injury.

2. **What happened because a go-between delivered ransom money to the supposed kidnapper?**

   Ⓐ The Lindberghs were given their son back.

   Ⓑ The go-between and the kidnapper took off together with the money.

   Ⓒ Charles Lindbergh received instructions on where to find his baby.

   Ⓓ The police arrested the kidnapper.

3. **Why was the Lindbergh family targeted?**

   Ⓐ They had made Hauptmann mad.

   Ⓑ They were wealthy.

   Ⓒ They had been randomly chosen.

   Ⓓ They didn't love their son.

4. **Why was Bruno Hauptmann convicted of the kidnapping and murder of Charles Lindbergh Jr.? Using complete sentences, summarize below the case against him in the prosecution's closing speech.**

   _____

   _____

   _____

   _____

   _____

   _____

   _____

   _____

USING CONTEXT CLUES

Skilled readers can often find the meaning of unfamiliar words by using *context clues*. This means they study the way the words are used in the text. Use the context clues in the excerpts below to determine the meaning of each **bold-faced** word. Then choose the answer that best matches the meaning of the word.

1. "It was time for another **routine** check."

CLUE: "Betty checked a short time later. At 10:00, Betty entered the nursery."

   Ⓐ usual

   Ⓑ surprise

   Ⓒ final

   Ⓓ plain

2. "By 11:00, the **investigation** was well under way."

CLUE: "The police found four main pieces of evidence."

   Ⓐ account

   Ⓑ judgment

   Ⓒ scene

   Ⓓ search

3. "The **nursemaid** was Betty Gow."

CLUE: "[Betty Gow] tidied up. She made sure the baby was covered."

   Ⓐ officer

   Ⓑ nanny

   Ⓒ cook

   Ⓓ housekeeper

4. "And his conviction should be **overturned**."

CLUE: "[Mrs. Hauptmann] believed her husband was framed."

   Ⓐ rolled

   Ⓑ upset

   Ⓒ reversed

   Ⓓ accepted

———————■———————

The Strange Case of Dr. Samuel Sheppard

Dr. Samuel Sheppard

by L. L. Owens

In 1954, Samuel Sheppard and his 30-year-old wife, Marilyn, lived in Bay Village, Ohio. Sheppard was a doctor. He was liked and respected in his community. Patients had nicknamed him "Dr. Sam."

[2] The Sheppards had a seven-year-old son named Sam. (They called him "Chip.") They happily awaited the birth of their second child.

[3] Bay Village was known as a lovely, quiet, and extremely safe suburb of Cleveland.

[4] Then a savage crime occurred in the Sheppards' lakeshore neighborhood.

[5] During the early hours of July 4, Marilyn was murdered. She was beaten to death in her bed.

[6] Sheppard was home when it happened. He woke up to find a stranger in the house, but it was too late to save his wife.

[7] When the police arrived on the scene, they questioned Sheppard. Sheppard told his version of the events leading up to—and those that came after—Marilyn's death.

[8] Sheppard and his wife entertained friends the evening of July 3. They all had a good time.

[9] Sheppard fell asleep watching television. Marilyn woke him when she went to bed.

[10] But Sheppard fell back to sleep. He was still on the couch when Marilyn cried out some hours later.

[11] Sheppard rushed upstairs. He saw a "dark form" with "bushy hair." It stood next to Marilyn's bed.

[12] He fought with the form.

Sheppard was knocked out by a blow to his neck.

[13]When he came to, Sheppard checked Marilyn's pulse. He couldn't find one. Marilyn was covered with blood.

[14]He ran to Chip's room. Thankfully, the boy was asleep—and safe.

[15]Sheppard heard a noise from the main floor. He hurried downstairs. The "form" ran out the back door.

[16]He chased the form to the lakeside beach. Sheppard said, "I lunged or jumped and grasped him . . . from the back."

[17]The two struggled. Sheppard was knocked out a second time.

[18]When he came to, the bottom half of his body was in the water of Lake Erie. The top half was clinging to the beach.

[19]He ran back home. He checked Marilyn's pulse again. Now, he knew, his wife was gone.

[20]Sheppard called neighbors Spencer and Esther Houk. Quickly, they arrived at the Sheppard home. They talked with Sheppard. And they saw the blood-spattered room where Marilyn lay dead. Then they notified the police.

[21]While the police searched the house, Sheppard's two brothers picked him up. The brothers were also doctors. The three of them went to their family-owned hospital. Sheppard was treated for injuries to his face and spinal cord.

[22]News of the crime filled Ohio newspapers. People were frightened. They couldn't believe such a thing could happen in Bay Village.

[23]The headlines painted a sympathetic picture of Dr. Sam. At first, people decided that the slaying was a freak happening. It was probably done by a wandering psychopath. It was definitely a stranger. Someone had intended to rob the Sheppard home but then got carried away.

[24]Sheppard's frequent media interviews helped further those beliefs. He expressed his deep sorrow at the loss of his life partner and his child's mother.

[25]He shared his utter amazement that someone could have come to Bay Village and committed this crime. He also offered a $10,000 reward to anyone who helped catch the killer.

[26]Soon, though, Samuel Sheppard was a suspect. His story varied little during the many times he'd told it. But to police it seemed unbelievable.

Sheppard's murder trial began on October 18, 1954.

[27]Then a woman named Susan Hayes came forward. She claimed to be Sheppard's secret girlfriend. She also claimed that Sheppard had talked of divorcing Marilyn.

[28]Public opinion changed as quickly as the news coverage. Headlines were different now. It was no surprise when the police arrested Sheppard and charged him with murder.

[29]Sheppard's murder trial began on October 18, 1954. The press crowded the courtroom. So did hordes of curious onlookers.

[30]The prosecution had no murder weapon. In fact, it had no real evidence connecting Sheppard with the crime. Prosecutor John Mahon offered Sheppard's relationship with Susan Hayes as a motive. Then he pointed out holes in Sheppard's story.

[31]Mahon raised many questions. He wanted to know why was there no sign of a break-in at the house. He also asked how Sheppard could have slept through the vicious attack on his wife. He wanted to know where the T-shirt was that Sheppard wore while entertaining guests the evening before the killing. Also, if Sheppard had passed out on the beach, why were no traces of sand found in his hair?

[32]The county coroner claimed to know what had made a bloody imprint found on Marilyn's pillow. He testified that it was formed by a two-bladed surgical instrument. It was assumed that Sheppard would be able to get this.

[33]From the beginning, Judge Edward Blythin thought Sheppard was guilty. He even went so far as to say so to a reporter—off the record. He made sure that he gave no favors to the defense.

[34]When the jury pronounced Sheppard guilty of second-degree murder, Judge Blythin quickly sentenced the doctor. He sentenced him to life imprisonment in the Ohio Penitentiary.

[35]Judge Blythin's actions had helped seal Sheppard's fate. But his

Crime and Punishment

careless comments to the reporter about Sheppard's guilt would eventually set Sheppard free.

[36]Attorney F. Lee Bailey heard about the judge's comments. He tried to prove that Sheppard had received an unfair trial.

[37]The Supreme Court agreed with Bailey. Sheppard's conviction was overturned. The court called it "prejudicial."

[38]So, in 1966, Sheppard stood trial again.

[39]Bailey was far better prepared than Sheppard's first team of defense attorneys.

[40]The prosecution presented basically the same case it had years earlier. The lawyers were not prepared to deal with F. Lee Bailey.

[41]Bailey skillfully raised doubts about each point in the prosecution's case. He even presented other ideas about murder suspects. His arguments were so powerful that the jury took note.

[42]The jury deliberated for just 12 hours. They found Sheppard not guilty. Sheppard was set free.

[43]However, his freedom was short-lived. Sheppard died just four years later. He was 46 years old. The cause of death was liver failure.

[44]Public interest in the case remained high in the decades following the murder trials. Many books and in-depth articles were written. Even a popular 1960s TV series and a hit 1993 movie were made. A remake of the TV series premiered in fall 2000. All were called *The Fugitive*. They were very loosely based on the Sheppard story.

[45]Sheppard's son, Chip (known in his adult life as Samuel Reese Sheppard), fought hard. He tried to solve his mother's murder. And he tried to completely clear his father's name.

[46]In 1995, Samuel filed a wrongful imprisonment suit against the state of Ohio. He sought $2 million in damages. He lost the case April 12, 2000.

[47]As of that day, Marilyn Sheppard's murder was still unsolved. And there were no new leads in sight.

If you have been timing your reading speed for this story, record your time below.

_____ : _____

Minutes   **Seconds**

UNDERSTANDING THE MAIN IDEA

The following questions will demonstrate your understanding of what the story is about, or the *main idea*. Choose the best answer for each question.

1. This story is mainly about

Ⓐ the murder trial of a prominent doctor.

Ⓑ a suburb in Cleveland.

Ⓒ the Sheppard family.

Ⓓ well-known attorney F. Lee Bailey.

2. The story could have been titled

Ⓐ "An Unusual Intruder."

Ⓑ "Victim or Murderer?"

Ⓒ "A Secret Girlfriend."

Ⓓ "Leading Lawyers."

3. Which detail supports the main idea of this story?

Ⓐ The Sheppards had a seven-year-old son named Sam.

Ⓑ Samuel Sheppard's brothers were also doctors.

Ⓒ Dr. Sheppard was arrested after Susan Hayes came forward.

Ⓓ The television program *The Fugitive* was based on the Sheppard story.

4. Find another detail that supports the main idea. Write it on the lines below.

_____

_____

_____

_____

RECALLING FACTS

The following questions will test how well you remember the facts in the story you just read. Choose the best answer for each question.

1. The story takes place

Ⓐ in a suburb of Cleveland.

Ⓑ near Lake Erie.

Ⓒ in Washington D.C.

Ⓓ in the mountains.

2. The first thing Dr. Sheppard did when he came to the first time was

Ⓐ run to his son's room.

Ⓑ hurry downstairs.

Ⓒ chase the intruder.

Ⓓ check on his wife.

3. After Dr. Sheppard ran back home, he immediately

Ⓐ called his neighbors.

Ⓑ called his brothers.

Ⓒ checked his wife's pulse.

Ⓓ called the police.

4. Dr. Sheppard's conviction was overturned by

Ⓐ the Supreme Court.

Ⓑ Judge Blythin.

Ⓒ the state of Ohio.

Ⓓ Bailey.

READING BETWEEN THE LINES

An *inference* is a conclusion drawn from facts. A *generalization* is a general statement, idea, or rule that is supported by facts. Analyze the story by choosing the best answer to each question below.

1. **What conclusion can you draw from paragraphs 33–35?**

   Ⓐ The judge was being paid by the prosecution.

   Ⓑ It is wrong for a judge to form an opinion before all the evidence is presented.

   Ⓒ The judge didn't care if the reporter quoted him in the newspaper about believing Sheppard was guilty.

   Ⓓ The judge believed Sheppard's story.

2. **What conclusion can you draw from paragraphs 40–42?**

   Ⓐ Bailey believed Dr. Sheppard was guilty.

   Ⓑ Bailey was a forceful, convincing attorney.

   Ⓒ Lawyers were prepared to deal with Bailey.

   Ⓓ The prosecution had a stronger case this time.

3. **What generalization can you make from this story?**

   Ⓐ All judges are prejudicial.

   Ⓑ Judges always form opinions on cases before the trials begin.

   Ⓒ Some judges are not impartial.

   Ⓓ Judges are careless by nature.

4. **It can be inferred from the story that**

   Ⓐ the public forgot about the Sheppard case soon after the trials.

   Ⓑ the Sheppard case still fascinates the public.

   Ⓒ Sheppard was definitely not guilty.

   Ⓓ Sheppard was definitely guilty.

DETERMINING CAUSE AND EFFECT

Choose the best answers for the following questions to show the relationship between what happened in the story (*effects*) and why those things happened (*causes*).

1. Because Judge Blythin made a careless comment,

Ⓐ the Supreme Court overturned Sheppard's conviction.

Ⓑ people believed Sheppard was innocent.

Ⓒ Sheppard was convicted.

Ⓓ Chip believed his father was innocent.

2. What happened because Susan Hayes claimed to be Dr. Sheppard's secret girlfriend?

Ⓐ Marilyn Sheppard was murdered.

Ⓑ Public opinion of Dr. Sheppard changed.

Ⓒ The public thought that the slaying was a freak happening.

Ⓓ Dr. Sheppard offered a reward to anyone who helped catch the killer.

3. Why was Susan Hayes an important witness?

Ⓐ She claimed that Sheppard had confessed to her.

Ⓑ She was a friend of Marilyn's.

Ⓒ She provided a motive.

Ⓓ She helped the defense.

4. Why was Dr. Sheppard's freedom short-lived?

Ⓐ He was soon arrested again for his wife's murder.

Ⓑ He soon committed another crime and was arrested.

Ⓒ He died just four years later.

Ⓓ He chose to go back to jail.

USING CONTEXT CLUES

Skilled readers can often find the meaning of unfamiliar words by using *context clues*. This means they study the way the words are used in the text. Use the context clues in the excerpts below to determine the meaning of each **bold-faced** word. Then choose the answer that best matches the meaning of the word.

1. "Then a **savage** crime occurred in the Sheppards' lakeshore neighborhood."

CLUE: "During the early hours of July 4, Marilyn was murdered."

Ⓐ common

Ⓑ vicious

Ⓒ petty

Ⓓ justified

2. "At first, people decided that the slaying was a **freak** happening."

CLUE: "It was probably done by a wandering psychopath . . . definitely a stranger."

Ⓐ abnormal

Ⓑ typical

Ⓒ planned

Ⓓ welcomed

3. "[Judge Blythin] sentenced [Dr. Sheppard] to life imprisonment in the Ohio **Penitentiary**." (paragraph 34)

Write what you think the bolded word means. Then record the context clues that led you to this definition.

Meaning:

_____

_____

_____

Context clues:

_____

_____

_____

4. "The jury **deliberated** for just 12 hours."

CLUE: "They found Sheppard not guilty. Sheppard was set free."

Ⓐ rested

Ⓑ vacationed

Ⓒ interviewed

Ⓓ debated

Kidnapping of an Heiress

by L. L. Owens

Patricia Hearst

Patricia Hearst was a smart, beautiful 19-year-old. She was a sophomore at the University of California at Berkeley. She was engaged to be married. And she was an heiress to the William Randolph Hearst newspaper empire.

[2] The Hearsts had been prominent on the American scene since the 1800s. The family had a history of involvement in business, media, politics, and charity.

[3] Patty's grandfather, William Randolph Hearst, was an important U.S. publisher. His publishing empire included 28 newspapers, 18 magazines, movie companies, news services, and radio stations.

[4] By the 1970s, Patty's father, Randolph Apperson Hearst, was the head of the Hearst empire. He was president and editor of the *San Francisco Examiner*. And he was an heir to his family's fortune. He had great clout in the publishing world.

[5] Patty's life took a strange and awful turn one February night in 1974. She was spending the evening at her apartment.

[6] A young woman tapped on the sliding-glass door. Patty's fiancé, Steven Weed, opened the door.

[7] The woman said, "May I use your telephone? There's been an accident."

[8] Weed believed for a moment that she needed help. Then the woman and two male members of the Symbionese Liberation Army (SLA) forced their way inside.

[9] They were heavily armed. They beat and tied up Weed.

[10] A neighbor heard the noise and tried to help. He was beaten too.

[11]The SLA left the apartment. And they took Patty with them. Patty kicked and screamed and fought the whole way.

[12]The kidnappers threw Patty into the trunk of a 1963 Chevrolet Impala. Then the two cars used by the SLA that night sped away. The SLA shot at the apartment house as they drove off.

[13]The SLA was known as a radical urban terrorist group. They had coined the word Symbionese. It was based on the biology term *symbiosis*. That means "the partnership of unlike groups for their mutual benefit." This was appropriate. Members of the group came from all different backgrounds. But they had one goal. According to their slogan, that goal was "Death to the fascist insect that preys upon the life of people!"

[14]The SLA likely had no more than a dozen members. A February 18, 1974, study pointed to some specialized skills among SLA members.

[15]The study was done by the Committee on Internal Security for the House of Representatives. It said that at least two members had had combat training. It also said that at least one member was a skilled machinist, and at least one had an extensive knowledge of language.

[16]Randolph and Catherine Hearst were Patty's parents. They were terrified at the news of her capture. They worried that their daughter would be further hurt or killed.

[17]The SLA had already been linked with other crimes, including murder. They claimed that kidnapping Patty was "part of its war against the fascist state."

[18]They also called it an act of revenge against the wealthy Hearsts. Yet they made no immediate demands of the family.

[19]On February 7, the SLA sent letters to a local radio station and an underground newspaper. The station also received a credit card stolen from Patty's apartment.

[20]The letter to the station began as follows. "Subject: Arrest and protective custody; and if necessary, execution. Target: Patricia Campbell Hearst, daughter of Randolph Hearst, corporate enemy of the people. Warrant issued by the court of the people."

[21]The letter claimed that Patty was unharmed. It also said, "Should any attempt be made to rescue the prisoner, or to arrest or harm any SLA element, the prisoner is to be

executed. . . . [Miss Hearst will be] maintained at adequate physical and mental condition [through] protective custody of combat and medical units . . . [Furthermore] all communications from this court must be published in full. In all newspapers. And all other forms of media. Failure to do so will endanger the safety of the prisoner."

[22] The SLA released a tape of Patty's voice on February 12. By now the country was riveted to the saga unfolding on the news.

[23] The tape helped reassure the Hearsts that Patty was alive. But they were still frightened.

[24] They heard a male voice on the tape. He said that he was willing to kill Patty. He considered it punishment.

[25] What was the punishment for? According to him, it was "for the crimes that her mother and father have by their actions committed against we, the American people and the oppressed people of the world."

[26] Soon the SLA released its demands. The members wanted money. But not for themselves.

[27] The group asked the Hearsts to give millions of dollars' worth of food. It was to go to all of California's poor, aged, disabled veterans, and ex-convicts.

[28] This was to be a sign of "good faith." The SLA would not talk about Patty's release until this happened.

[29] Randolph offered to give $2 million to California's needy. Then, he promised, he'd give another $4 million—but only if Patty was safely released.

[30] Randolph followed through. Truckloads of food arrived for distribution. People fought one another to get to the food. Riots nearly broke out.

[31] But Patty Hearst was not set free. The SLA failed to keep its promise.

[32] Patty's life as an SLA prisoner was horrifying. To begin with, she was reportedly locked in a closet for weeks.

[33] According to Patty's 1982 book, *Every Secret Thing*, she was tortured, raped, and brainwashed. This meant that the SLA forced her to change her thoughts and beliefs.

[34] Two months after Patty's abduction, the nation gasped. They saw new images of her. Photos of Patty had surfaced in the newspapers.

[35] Thankfully, she was alive. But Patty was now called "Tania." And she carried a rifle and wore combat gear. News reports claimed Patty had

joined the SLA. She had even helped her captors rob a San Francisco bank!

[36]Patty's family and the nation had feared for Patty's safety. Authorities had been searching for her, hoping to rescue her.

[37]Then, out of the blue, Patty showed up at a bank. But she didn't appear to be in distress. She was robbing and threatening people.

[38]In two months, Patricia Hearst seemed to go from innocent kidnapping victim to armed terrorist. The whole situation was bizarre.

[39]On May 17, 1974, the SLA was involved in a Los Angeles house fire and a shootout with police. Six SLA members were killed.

[40]Meanwhile, Patty had disappeared. She and at least two other SLA members had fled. They crossed the country. They went as far east as New York.

[41]On September 18, 1975, Patty was back in San Francisco. The FBI captured her and three other SLA members that day.

[42]Patty was arrested for armed robbery.

[43]Patty's trial began on February 4, 1976. This was exactly two years after she was kidnapped.

[44]The Hearsts had hired attorney F. Lee Bailey. Bailey was confident that he could defend Patty.

[45]Bailey presented Patty as a "prisoner of war." He said that she had taken part in SLA's activities for one reason only. She had wanted to stay alive.

[46]Prosecutor James Browning Jr. argued his case. He said that Patty had always known what she was doing. He said she had willingly participated in the robbery and other SLA events.

[47]Patty took the stand in her own defense. She testified that her participation in the crimes was the only way she could have survived.

[48]Some expert witnesses backed this up. Others testified to the contrary. They said Patty had enjoyed the fame and excitement that becoming SLA's "Tania" had given her.

[49]Meanwhile, the public didn't understand. How could Patty have been brainwashed? They followed the trial closely, from beginning to end, hoping to find out.

[50]The press reported damaging evidence against Patty. Public opinion was split.

[51]On March 20, 1976, the jury found Patricia Hearst guilty as charged. She was sentenced to seven years in prison.

[52]Patty was in and out of jail for three years as her case was appealed. She was released for good on February 1, 1979. President Jimmy Carter commuted her sentence. He believed that she had suffered greatly. He felt that she never would have committed criminal acts had she not been forced to.

[53]By 2000, Carter had asked both President George Bush Sr. and President Bill Clinton to grant Hearst a full pardon. Carter said that since her release from prison "[Patty] has been a model citizen in every way."

[54]In January 2001, President Clinton pardoned Hearst right before he left office.

President Jimmy Carter commuted Hearst's sentence.

If you have been timing your reading speed for this story, record your time below.

_____ : _____

Minutes   ***Seconds***

UNDERSTANDING THE MAIN IDEA

The following questions will demonstrate your understanding of what the story is about, or the *main idea*. Choose the best answer for each question.

1. This story is mainly about

Ⓐ the William Randolph Hearst family.

Ⓑ Patty Hearst and the SLA.

Ⓒ a bank robbery in San Francisco.

Ⓓ Patty Hearst's trial.

2. The story could have been titled

Ⓐ "Guilty or Innocent?"

Ⓑ "A Family Fortune."

Ⓒ "Ransom Money."

Ⓓ "Seven Years in Prison."

3. Which detail best supports the main idea of this story?

Ⓐ Patty Hearst was a smart, beautiful 19-year-old.

Ⓑ The Symbionese Liberation Army took credit for kidnapping Patty.

Ⓒ Randolph Apperson Hearst was president of the *San Francisco Examiner*.

Ⓓ Patty was engaged to Steven Weed.

4. Find another detail that supports the main idea. Write it on the lines below.

_____

_____

_____

_____

RECALLING FACTS

The following questions will test how well you remember the facts in the story you just read. Choose the best answer for each question.

1. Randolph Apperson Hearst had great power in the

Ⓐ movie industry.

Ⓑ news services.

Ⓒ publishing world.

Ⓓ radio stations.

2. After kidnapping Patty Hearst, the SLA first

Ⓐ made demands for money.

Ⓑ sent letters to a radio station.

Ⓒ sent a letter to the Hearst family.

Ⓓ threatened to kill Patty.

3. Two months after Patty Hearst was kidnapped, she showed up

Ⓐ at her parents' home.

Ⓑ in Los Angeles.

Ⓒ in New York.

Ⓓ at a bank.

4. Patty Hearst was arrested for

Ⓐ first-degree murder.

Ⓑ kidnapping.

Ⓒ armed robbery.

Ⓓ conspiracy to commit a kidnapping.

READING BETWEEN THE LINES

An *inference* is a conclusion drawn from facts. A *generalization* is a general statement, idea, or rule that is supported by facts. Analyze the story by choosing the best answer to each question below.

1. **What conclusion can you draw from paragraphs 6–11?**

   Ⓐ The SLA was dangerous.

   Ⓑ The SLA was ineffective and insecure.

   Ⓒ No one was hurt during the kidnapping.

   Ⓓ It was difficult for the SLA to kidnap Patty.

2. **What conclusion can you draw from paragraphs 21–27?**

   Ⓐ Patty Hearst was being punished because her family had violated the law.

   Ⓑ Patty Hearst was being punished because her family was wealthy.

   Ⓒ The SLA was not interested in helping the poor.

   Ⓓ The SLA did not condone violence.

3. **What generalization can you make from this story?**

   Ⓐ Some people believe that Patty Hearst was guilty.

   Ⓑ Everyone believes that Patty Hearst was innocent.

   Ⓒ All government officials believed Patty Hearst was guilty.

   Ⓓ No one believed Patty Hearst's story.

4. **It can be inferred from the story that the members of the SLA were**

   Ⓐ all foreign.

   Ⓑ determined to get attention.

   Ⓒ committed to upholding the law.

   Ⓓ supporters of the government.

——— ■ ———

DETERMINING CAUSE AND EFFECT

Choose the best answers for the following questions to show the relationship between what happened in the story (*effects*) and why those things happened (*causes*).

1. **Because the SLA members wanted to get to Patty Hearst,**

   Ⓐ they tricked Patty's fiancé into letting them in her apartment.

   Ⓑ two SLA members fled to New York.

   Ⓒ they waited until Patty was alone.

   Ⓓ Patty and two SLA members fled to San Francisco.

2. **What happened because the SLA demanded millions of dollars in food be given to the needy?**

   Ⓐ Patty Hearst was released by the SLA.

   Ⓑ Randolph Apperson Hearst gave $2 million in food and demanded that Patty be set free before he gave more.

   Ⓒ The SLA killed Patty Hearst.

   Ⓓ The SLA called Patty Hearst "Tania."

3. **Why did F. Lee Bailey claim that Patty Hearst had taken part in SLA's activities?**

   Ⓐ She wanted to get back at her parents.

   Ⓑ She believed in their cause.

   Ⓒ She enjoyed the excitement and fame.

   Ⓓ She wanted to stay alive.

4. **Why did the terrorist group choose Symbionese as part of their name? Explain below, using complete sentences.**

   _____

   _____

   _____

   _____

   _____

   _____

   _____

   _____■_____

USING CONTEXT CLUES

Skilled readers can often find the meaning of unfamiliar words by using *context clues*. This means they study the way the words are used in the text. Use the context clues in the excerpts below to determine the meaning of each **bold-faced** word. Then choose the answer that best matches the meaning of the word.

1. "The Hearsts had been **prominent** on the American scene since the 1800s."

CLUE: "The family had a history of involvement in business, media, politics, and charity."

  Ⓐ unnoticed

  Ⓑ peculiar

  Ⓒ famous

  Ⓓ humble

2. "[Randolph Apperson Hearst] had great **clout** in the publishing world."

CLUE: "He was president and editor of the *San Francisco Examiner*. And he was an heir to his family's fortune."

  Ⓐ mistrust

  Ⓑ influence

  Ⓒ inexperience

  Ⓓ hatred

3. "The SLA was known as a **radical** urban terrorist group."

CLUE: " . . . at least two members had had combat training. . . . The SLA had already been linked with other crimes, including murder."

  Ⓐ entire

  Ⓑ basic

  Ⓒ mild

  Ⓓ extreme

4. "Some expert witnesses backed this up [that Patty Hearst had participated in the crimes to survive]. Others testified to the **contrary**."

CLUE: "[The others] said Patty had enjoyed the fame and excitement that becoming SLA's 'Tania' had given her."

  Ⓐ opposite

  Ⓑ extreme

  Ⓒ maximum

  Ⓓ same

Senseless Destruction

The Oklahoma City Bombing

by L. L. Owens

Timothy McVeigh

On April 19, 1995, people in Oklahoma City started their day. Busy people rushed to work. Kids went to school. It was business as usual—at least, it was until 9:03 a.m. That's when everything changed.

[2]A bomb exploded. It was in a rental truck downtown. The truck was parked outside the nine-story Alfred P. Murrah Federal Building. The building was destroyed.

[3]There were 168 deaths. Many of the victims were small children.

[4]Rescue efforts went on for two weeks. Many people worked tirelessly to find survivors. It was a difficult job, often under dangerous conditions.

[5]But rescue teams didn't give up. They saved lives. Some survivors were trapped in the rubble. Their injuries made it impossible for them to move. Sometimes they couldn't even speak.

[6]The senseless destruction angered the entire nation. It seemed that all Americans mourned with the bombing victims' families. It was horrible. "Unfathomable" was often used to describe the situation.

[7]Ninety minutes after the explosion, Timothy McVeigh was pulled over. An Oklahoma Highway Patrol officer noticed that McVeigh's car had no license plate.

[8]Two days later, McVeigh was identified as a suspect in the bombing. He was 27 years old.

[9]Soon McVeigh's friend, Terry Nichols, was also under suspicion. Nichols and McVeigh were good friends. They had been in the army together.

[10]Nichols decided to turn himself in. He surrendered to police in Kansas.

[11]The case against McVeigh and Nichols was strong. Their actions were retraced. There was a lot of evidence. Evidence included phone records, bills, explosives, and other items that linked the two men to each other—and to the crime.

[12]The grand jury concluded that the men "knowingly, intentionally, willfully, and maliciously" worked together and with unknown others to commit this terrible crime.

[13]Here's how McVeigh and Nichols made it happen. The men planned an act of violence against persons and property of the United States. They then selected the Alfred P. Murrah Federal Building and its occupants as the targets and asked others to help. Then they obtained and hid the pieces of a truck bomb. They used stolen property to help finance their crimes. They used false names to conceal their activities. They built an explosive truck bomb, and Timothy McVeigh placed the bomb outside the Alfred P. Murrah Federal Building in downtown Oklahoma City. Finally, he set off the bomb.

[14]McVeigh and Nichols were both charged with the bombing. A federal grand jury in Oklahoma City handed down the indictments. The two men would stand trial on 11 federal charges. Count 1 was for conspiracy to use a weapon of mass destruction. Count 2 was for use of a weapon of mass destruction. Count 3 was for destruction by explosive. And counts 4–11 were for first-degree murder (for the deaths of eight federal workers).

[15]The Oklahoma City bombing is known as the worst terrorist attack on U.S. soil. A May 17, 1995, *New York Times* article said that McVeigh admitted to the bombing. It said that he told two people that he did it. And he told them why he chose the Alfred P. Murrah Federal Building. He chose it because it housed numerous government offices and it was less architecturally stable than other federal buildings.

[16]McVeigh and Nichols meant to cause harm. They meant to kill people. They also meant to shock the nation.

[17]Why? They felt that the U.S. government deserved to be punished. They did not care that helpless, innocent people—including small children—would die.

[18]Five years after the crime, McVeigh was interviewed for the

An Oklahoma City police car with a small American flag and a message sat near the Alfred P. Murrah Federal Building nearly a week after the bombing.

CBS newsmagazine *60 Minutes*. The interview was taped February 22, 2000.

[19]McVeigh said of the year 1995, "I believe I had anger welling in me."

[20]For one thing, he was angry at trying out for and failing to get into the army's special forces unit. He was also upset over his role in the Gulf War. He felt that he'd had no right to enter another land and kill enemy soldiers—even as part of war.

[21]McVeigh was further angered by the handling of two federal cases. One of the cases occurred in 1992 when a federal agent killed the wife and son of white supremacist Randy Weaver. There had been a standoff in Ruby Ridge, Idaho. A judge dismissed manslaughter charges against the agent. This upset McVeigh. He said, "Federal agents

taking the role of judge, jury, and executioner . . . [Then] you have these . . . federal agents not held accountable. They become immune from the law."

[22]Another case involved the 1993 "siege at Waco [Texas]." Seventy Branch Davidians, members of a religious sect, died in a fire. There had been a 51-day standoff with federal agents. McVeigh said that he was "shaken, disillusioned, angered that that could happen in this country." He said, "You deprived them of life, liberty, and property. You didn't guarantee [their] rights. You deprived them of them."

[23]Asked during the interview if he would like to do anything differently, McVeigh said, "I think anybody in life says, 'I wish I could've gone back and done this differently, done that differently.' There are moments, but not one that stands out."

[24]The trials were held in Denver, Colorado. The public watched McVeigh's and Nichols' trials closely. People hoped that justice would be served.

[25]Both men were convicted of their federal crimes. But they received different sentences.

[26]McVeigh was convicted of murder and conspiracy to commit murder. He was also found guilty of the weapons-related charges against him. His sentence was the death penalty.

[27]Nichols was convicted of conspiracy to use a weapon of mass destruction and eight counts of involuntary manslaughter.

[28]The jury could not agree on a sentence for Nichols. So it became U.S. District Judge Richard Matsch's decision. He did not have authority to sentence Nichols to death. He sentenced him to life in prison without the possibility of parole.

[29]Nichols showed no emotion when he heard his sentence. Judge Matsch called Nichols a "proven enemy of the Constitution."

If you have been timing your reading speed for this story, record your time below.

_____ : _____

Minutes   **Seconds**

Crime and Punishment

UNDERSTANDING THE MAIN IDEA

The following questions will demonstrate your understanding of what the story is about, or the *main idea*. Choose the best answer for each question.

1. This story is mainly about

Ⓐ Oklahoma City.

Ⓑ a horrifying terrorist act.

Ⓒ the making of a bomb.

Ⓓ the decision of a judge.

2. The story could have been titled

Ⓐ "An Act of Violence."

Ⓑ "Timothy McVeigh's Interview."

Ⓒ "Surrender in Kansas."

Ⓓ "Army Buddies."

3. Which detail best supports the main idea of this story?

Ⓐ Rescue teams worked for two weeks to save victims.

Ⓑ Timothy McVeigh and Terry Nichols were good friends.

Ⓒ Seventy Branch Davidians had died in Waco, Texas, in 1993.

Ⓓ The Alfred P. Murrah Federal Building was in Oklahoma City, Oklahoma.

4. Find another detail that supports the main idea. Write it on the lines below.

_____

_____

_____

_____

RECALLING FACTS

The following questions will test how well you remember the facts in the story you just read. Choose the best answer for each question.

1. The bomb was hidden inside a

Ⓐ bathroom.

Ⓑ package in the mail.

Ⓒ rental truck.

Ⓓ briefcase.

2. Timothy McVeigh was pulled over by the Oklahoma Highway Patrol because he

Ⓐ was speeding.

Ⓑ had called the police and confessed.

Ⓒ had no license plate.

Ⓓ was driving the rental truck that had housed the bomb.

3. Timothy McVeigh was upset over his role in

Ⓐ the Gulf War.

Ⓑ the Vietnam War.

Ⓒ the Korean War.

Ⓓ the siege at Waco, Texas.

4. Timothy McVeigh was sentenced to

Ⓐ 50 years in prison.

Ⓑ life in prison.

Ⓒ death.

Ⓓ a mental hospital.

READING BETWEEN THE LINES

An *inference* is a conclusion drawn from facts. A *generalization* is a general statement, idea, or rule that is supported by facts. Analyze the story by choosing the best answer to each question below.

1. What conclusion can you draw from paragraph 13?

Ⓐ Nichols knew he was a suspect in the bombing.

Ⓑ Nichols knew McVeigh from childhood.

Ⓒ McVeigh and Nichols had carefully planned their attack.

Ⓓ McVeigh and Nichols were the only two involved in the bombing.

2. What conclusion can you draw from paragraph 23?

Ⓐ Timothy McVeigh was sorry for what he had done.

Ⓑ Timothy McVeigh showed no remorse for the crime.

Ⓒ Timothy McVeigh had committed other crimes in the past.

Ⓓ Timothy McVeigh would do things differently if given the chance.

3. What generalization about terrorism can be made after reading this story?

_____

_____

_____

_____

_____

_____

_____

4. It can be inferred from the story that

Ⓐ McVeigh and Nichols considered themselves enemies of the government.

Ⓑ McVeigh and Nichols had acted rashly, without forethought.

Ⓒ McVeigh and Nichols had murdered before.

Ⓓ McVeigh and Nichols only wanted to harm people, not kill them.

DETERMINING CAUSE AND EFFECT

Choose the best answers for the following questions to show the relationship between what happened in the story (*effects*) and why those things happened (*causes*).

1. **Because 168 people died in the Oklahoma City Bombing,**

   Ⓐ McVeigh and Nichols were let off with a light sentence.

   Ⓑ the government held a siege in Waco, Texas.

   Ⓒ it is known as the worst terrorist attack on U.S. soil.

   Ⓓ many of the victims were small children.

2. **What happened because the jury could not agree on a sentence for Terry Nichols?**

   Ⓐ He was set free for life.

   Ⓑ Another jury took their place.

   Ⓒ The jury decided to give him whatever sentence McVeigh received.

   Ⓓ A U.S. District judge sentenced him to life without parole.

3. **Why did Timothy McVeigh and Terry Nichols choose the Alfred P. Murrah Federal Building?**

   Ⓐ They had both worked there.

   Ⓑ It was architecturally unstable.

   Ⓒ It was the most famous federal building.

   Ⓓ Children were inside.

4. **Why was Timothy McVeigh upset about the handling of two federal cases?**

   Ⓐ He had family involved in both cases.

   Ⓑ He believed that federal agents were not given enough power to act however they saw fit.

   Ⓒ He had wanted to participate as a federal agent and was not allowed to do so.

   Ⓓ He thought federal agents were not held accountable for their actions.

USING CONTEXT CLUES

Skilled readers can often find the meaning of unfamiliar words by using *context clues*. This means they study the way the words are used in the text. Use the context clues in the excerpts below to determine the meaning of each **bold-faced** word. Then choose the answer that best matches the meaning of the word.

1. " '**Unfathomable**' was often used to describe the situation."

CLUE: "It seemed that all Americans mourned with the bombing victims' families. The senseless destruction angered the entire nation."

Ⓐ enormous

Ⓑ uncertain

Ⓒ unexplainable

Ⓓ predictable

2. " 'They become **immune** from the law.' "

CLUE: " '[Then] you have these . . . federal agents not held accountable.' "

Ⓐ powerless

Ⓑ protected

Ⓒ dependent

Ⓓ opposed

3. "A May 17, 1995, *New York Times* article said that McVeigh **admitted** to the bombing."

CLUE: "It said that he told two people that he did it."

Ⓐ confessed

Ⓑ allowed

Ⓒ permitted

Ⓓ agreed

4. "Both men were convicted of their federal crimes. But they received different **sentences**."

CLUE: "[McVeigh's] sentence was the death penalty. . . . [Judge Matsch] sentenced [Nichols] to life in prison without the possibility of parole."

Ⓐ opinions

Ⓑ phrases

Ⓒ results

Ⓓ punishments

— ▬ —

End-of-Unit Activities

1. **Choose one of the four trials featured in this unit. Imagine you are a jury member. You have finished deliberating, and the verdict has been announced. Answer the reporter's questions below. Make sure you offer details to support your answers.**

Explain how it felt to be on the jury for such an important trial.

_____

_____

_____

_____

Are you satistfied with the verdict and the sentence? Was justice served?

_____

_____

_____

_____

Which facts or what evidence was most conclusive in your mind?

_____

_____

_____

_____

Explain your feelings toward the defendant now that the trial is over.

_____

_____

_____

_____

End-of-Unit Activities

2. **Rank each of the stories in this unit, from the one you liked the most to the one you liked the least. For each story, write one interesting fact you learned. Then tell why you liked the story you ranked _1_ the best.**

LESSON 9 Ranking _____

_____

_____

_____

_____

LESSON 10 Ranking _____

_____

_____

_____

_____

LESSON 11 Ranking _____

_____

_____

_____

_____

LESSON 12 Ranking _____

_____

_____

_____

_____

Why did you like the story you ranked _1_ the best?

_____

_____

_____

_____

Crime and Punishment

Words-Per-Minute Chart

Directions:

Use the chart to find your words-per-minute reading speed. Refer to the reading time you recorded at the end of each article. Find your reading time in seconds along the left-hand side of the chart or minutes and seconds along the right-hand side of the chart. Your words-per-minute score will be listed next to the time in the column below the appropriate lesson number.

No. of Words	Lesson 9 982	Lesson 10 1154	Lesson 11 1428	Lesson 12 995	
80	737	866	1071	746	1:20
100	589	692	857	597	1:40
120	491	577	714	498	2:00
140	421	495	612	426	2:20
160	368	433	536	373	2:40
180	327	385	476	332	3:00
200	295	346	428	299	3:20
220	268	315	389	271	3:40
240	246	289	357	249	4:00
260	227	266	330	230	4:20
280	210	247	306	213	4:40
300	196	231	286	199	5:00
320	184	216	268	187	5:20
340	173	204	252	176	5:40
360	164	192	238	166	6:00
380	155	182	225	157	6:20
400	147	173	214	149	6:40
420	140	165	204	142	7:00
440	134	157	195	136	7:20
460	128	151	186	130	7:40
480	123	144	179	124	8:00
500	118	138	171	119	8:20
520	113	133	165	115	8:40
540	109	128	159	111	9:00
560	105	124	153	107	9:20
580	102	119	148	103	9:40
600	98	115	143	100	10:00
620	95	112	138	96	10:20
640	92	108	134	93	10:40
660	89	105	130	90	11:00
680	87	102	126	88	11:20
700	84	99	122	85	11:40
720	82	96	119	83	12:00
740	80	94	116	81	12:20
760	78	91	113	79	12:40
780	76	89	110	77	13:00
800	74	87	107	75	13:20
820	72	84	104	73	13:40
840	70	82	102	71	14:00

Seconds

Minutes and Seconds